A CHANGE OF HEART

A CHANGE OF HEART

LAWRENCE A. DECKER

KROSHKA BOOKS
COMMACK, NY

Graphics: Frank Grucci & John M. T'lustachowski
Editorial Production: Susan Boriotti
Book Production: Donna Dennis and Tammy Sauter
Acquisitions Director: Tatiana Shohov
Circulation: Cathy DeGregory and Maryanne Schmidt
Office Manager: Annette Hellinger

Library of Congress Cataloging-in-Publication Data

  p. cm.
ISBN 1-56072-526-5

1. Life Changing Event- Psychological Aspects. 2.
Change (Psychological) 3. Heart Diseases--Patients--
Psychology. I.Title.

BF 637.L53D43 1998   97-32524
616.1'206--dc21   CIP

Copyright © 1998 Lawrence A. Decker

  Kroshka Books a Division of:
  Nova Science Publishers, Inc.
  6080 Jericho Turnpike, Suite 207
  Commack, New York 11725
  Tele. 516-499-3103 Fax 516-499-3146
  E Mail Novascience@earthlink.net

Printed in the United States of America

DEDICATION

This book is dedicated to my wife Louise,
my children, Jay and Elena, to my sister, Barbara,
and to the memory of my parents,
Dr. Robert Jay Decker and Jeanette Estrin Decker.

CONTENTS

A CHANGE OF HEART

"There is no instinct like that of the heart."
Lord Byron

Heart disease kills more people in America than all other diseases combined. Billions of dollars a year are spent in treatment. The disease affects not only sufferers, but also family members, friends, colleagues, employers and health care companies. Millions of people see professionals every day for symptoms such as high blood pressure or angina. Almost a million people in the U.S. undergo invasive procedures such as by-pass surgery or angioplasty each year. Recently I became one of these people.

Through the years, my doctors often recommended that I make certain lifestyle changes such as reducing stress, improving my diet, and exercising more. Despite my attempts to follow the advice being offered to me, I seemed to have a difficult time sticking with my doctor's recommendations. Good intentions to watch my food intake and exercise habits, for example, often gave way to past bad habits. I was left feeling confused and guilty as to why I didn't follow recommendations even though my life could depend upon it. Finally it became necessary that I undergo major surgery. Since I knew that one-third to one-half of arteries opened with angioplasty become blocked again after four to six months, and up to half of by-pass grafts re-occlude after only five years, I decided it was high time that I confronted whatever was going on in my mind before it killed me.

It became necessary for me to look at my own role in the formation and maintenance of my disease. I discovered that I could not easily change my ways because of my personality makeup. Upon honest reflection, I realized I was a "tough customer" when it came to following advice. Only when I began to explore the components of my personality—the distortions in my self-image, thinking patterns, belief system, behavior and feeling states—was I able to regain my courage, rediscover my essential self, and create my life anew.

Individuals who learn that they are at risk for heart disease, who are experiencing hypertension, arrhythmia, circulatory disorders and angina, or who have had, or are about to have angioplasty, or bypass surgery would benefit from reading this book.

WHY I WROTE THIS BOOK

As a child I used to sit terrified in a corner as my father screamed out in pain for my mother to administer more morphine. Many hospitalizations, open heart surgery, and daily dialysis resulted in a life which could have easily been called tragic. Yet my father was a hero to me, becoming a psychologist late in life despite being completely disabled according to the government. I could not watch him transform from a supposed "vegetable" to a productive member of society, from a rage-filled and pain-wracked individual to a gentle, understanding and loving man without asking myself a lot of questions. I became a psychologist in part to understand how people can overcome seemingly insurmountable obstacles, and change themselves at the deepest possible levels.

During my 20 years in private practice as a psychologist, I saw a number of patients who came for treatment because of their need to adjust to their physical illness. I became convinced that, like my father, these individuals had a great deal to do with their own illness and, given the tools, could tap into deep reservoirs within themselves to heal. While leading a group of heart patients in a cardiology clinic, I was impressed with the number of similarities in their backgrounds, experiences, thinking patterns and belief systems. It was as if they had belonged to a club that they didn't know that they joined. This "heart disease club" has a number of unspoken rules which negatively impact upon the health of each member. These unwritten rules of conduct impact upon the quality of the member's lives as well as on their potential to be all that is possible for them.

When I discovered that I, too, had serious heart disease, I was challenged to confront my own set of unwritten rules and beliefs that contributed to my condition. This book, representative of my journey into self-understanding, is written with the hope that you too may learn to recognize damaging patterns of thinking, feeling and behaving. By doing so, perhaps you can prevent your heart condition from worsening.

I will never forget my shock at learning that like my father before me, I would require surgery. I went through a period of anxiety and fear, followed by episodes of depression, even before the operation was scheduled. My primary-care physician, both cardiologists, as well as the surgeon chosen to perform the operation were all kind and caring individuals. However, they tended to view my condition from their own areas of training and expertise. There was no ombudsman who represented Larry Decker, the whole person. There were no suggestions regarding the kinds of feelings I would most likely face, and what I could do about them. Nor was there an appreciation of the emotional factors that may have contributed to my heart disease. That I had thought of myself in unrealistic ways my entire life, adopted unhealthy lifestyle patterns, and had guilty feelings about behaviors that contributed to my condition, were areas that could not be addressed in the minutes we had available to us. I was left alone to sort out my feelings, while I waited for the surgery to be scheduled. I struggled desperately to get myself into the proper frame of mind for surgery, knowing as a psychologist that the outcome of surgery is often influenced by the emotional state of the patient.

This book was also written in the hope that professional people will become more sensitive to the emotional factors that contribute to the development of heart disease , and influence the intervention and recovery stages as well. Research indicates that depression increases the risk of heart disease in adults. Investigators have found that depression begins fairly early in heart patients, perhaps in their twenties. I believe that people do not develop depression out of the blue when they reach their twenties, but rather, undiagnosed depression may already exist in childhood, which loads the deck in favor of developing heart disease later. It is my hope that this book will sensitize professionals to looking for and recognizing childhood depression in order to treat this condition before it can develop into later physical problems. Patients and their families will also benefit by having a better understanding of these important areas. Physicians, cardiologists, teachers, nurses, psychologists, social workers and concerned loved ones would be interested in what I learned as well.

There are many self-help books packed with useful information in the area of heart disease which are very helpful to the interested reader,. While a great deal of good can come from factual information, there is a danger that these books may falsely imply that information about diet, exercise, etc. is all that is needed to combat heart disease. If things were that simple, there would be less need for repeat visits to doctors for lifestyle abuses, and less need for repeat surgical procedures. *Knowing* what's good for you and *doing* what's good for you are two different things. Even doing what's good for you is tenuous if the motivation comes from such external sources as doctor's orders or a spouse's complaints. *A Change of Heart* builds upon the work of two physicians who have been pioneers in the field of cardiology, and who have recognized the importance of psychological factors in the formation and development of heart disease.

Dr. Dean Ornish's Program for reversing heart disease gives information that is useful to heart patients, such as meditation, visualization, prayer, relaxation and stretching. He acknowledges that changing behavior is not always enough for real healing to occur, however. "We need to address what underlies the behavior. It's not sufficient to simply change behaviors like diet and exercise, because our behaviors are only manifestations of our self-perceptions." I saw a need for a book which helps patients to unravel their self-perceptions.

An excellent book by Bruno Cortis, MD, attempts to empower patients to take charge of their own healing. Dr. Cortis lists seven keys to a healthy heart and five keys for healthy living. His book, *Heart and Soul,* is an excellent overview of those areas that need to be addressed for thorough and comprehensive changes to occur in the heart patient. Dr. Cortis was unable in the space allotted him, to delve more deeply into the workings of the "self", which he regards as the cause of heart disease. I felt after reading his book that the thinking patterns, belief systems and defensive strategies of the heart patient needed to be addressed in more detail. The distinction between operating from one's essential self as opposed to one's cultural identity, became the focus of my own work.

I am indebted to these authors and consider my own work to follow upon their beliefs that the "self" and "self-perceptions" need to be adequately addressed. I have attempted to provide a blueprint for recognizing and changing who a person is *being,* not just what he *does*, as a means to assure that the patient adheres to his or her desired goals.

A Change of Heart helps heart patients see themselves in a new light, as bigger than they ever thought themselves to be, as more powerful than they ever imagined, and more connected to others than they ever dared to think.

In the following chapters, we will address the change process. We will learn ways of overcoming resistance to change, of tapping into motivations for change, and of identifying methods to increase the likelihood that desired changes will stick. We will learn to recognize and transform damaging aspects of our personalities. We will also learn ways to create new patterns of thought to replace conditioned, automatic thinking as well as ways to change negative beliefs, and the behaviors that flow from these beliefs. Heart patients will learn to operate from the position of *having* beliefs that can be examined and disputed rather than *being* their beliefs, which makes them so integrated within the fabric of who they are, that they cannot see the forest for the trees. Finally the book teaches individuals with heart disease how to create a future which is not made up of more of the same. Rather, they will learn how to live their lives in the present, based upon their unique view of the future that they can choose to live into. That future gives them new purpose and direction, and opens new possibilities in the present.

He is the best physician who is the most ingenious inspirer of hope.
John Bunyan

ACKNOWLEDGMENT

This book would not have been possible without the contributions of many people who have touched my heart. Observing my patients overcome obstacles and push through barriers, taught me to hear the quiet whispers of my higher self, edging me forward.

My father became a hero to me and an inspiration. He gave me the tools needed to be successful in the world, but more importantly, demonstrated the power of love in his own transformation.

My mother was a source of hope for me. Her smile radiated from deep within, and warmed the heart of everyone she touched.

I acknowledge my friend, Dr. Jeffery Weiner, for pushing me to personalize a book which was more comfortably written in a pedantic style.

Dr. Howard Savin, my friend and former partner, kept me balanced with one foot in reality as the book progressed.

Mark Magerman and David Lieberman are two friends who allowed me to try out ideas and offered me valued feedback.

I thank Irv Mac Dowell, an excellent writer, teacher and editor, for helping me to complete this book.

I have been inspired by the work of Dr. Deepak Chopra, Dr. Dean Ornish, and Dr. Bruno Cortis.

To my wife Louise, who has been the source of light in my life, thank you for your guidance and patience in helping me to face my fears of intimacy.

Thanks to my loving son, Jay, who has helped me to heal some of my own wounds, and to experience the joy, excitement and magic of life again.

Thanks to my daughter Elena, for introducing me to the feelings of love when she was born, and for demonstrating, by her example, the essence of creativity and originality.

Thanks to my sister, Barbara Zerby, for seeing beneath her big brother's sometimes maddening behaviors, and for her unflagging support and encouragement.

CHAPTER 1

A CHANGE OF HEART

There are many tears in the heart that never reach the eye.
Anonymous

I experienced a change of heart on January 16, 1997, the day that I had quadruple by-pass surgery. While four new arteries relieved my chest pain, it was my intention to understand and change *myself* that would make the greatest difference in my life. I had twenty years of practice as a clinical psychologist which was helpful in my quest. In addition, I had co-founded a managed mental healthcare company that covered several million lives, and had worked as a consultant to a leading Health Maintenance Organization and also to a large cardiology practice. Thus, I felt prepared to tackle the difficult issue of my own role in the creation of heart disease.

I had exercised regularly for several years and tried to eat mostly vegetarian meals, and yet I was still unable to prevent heart disease. I was told by several cardiologists that my condition was hereditary. My father had quadruple by-pass surgery, and several close relatives died from heart disease. Perhaps my cardiologist encouraged me to believe, "It's all in the genes," to alleviate my guilt that I had not done enough. But the message had the effect of making me feel more helpless. After all, what could I do about my genes?

I was even more confused when I learned that many Americans start to form plaque in their arteries at an early age, yet not all experience debilitating symptoms. Even at mid-life, there are many people with clogged arteries who never see their doctor for symptoms associated with heart disease. It is also well known that many individuals have heart attacks despite having none of the customary risk factors, such as high cholesterol or a family history of heart disease. It has been estimated that the standard risk factors such as smoking, excess weight, genetics, and lack of exercise, are present in only 50 percent of heart patients. This leaves a very big question begging to be answered. How can we explain the presence of heart disease in millions of people who have none of the known risk factors? Could there be something about the psychology of the individual that leads to heart disease? Dr. Meyer Friedman and Dr. Ray Rosenman found that men with Type-A personality characteristics (hard-driving, competitive, hostile) were twice as likely to develop heart disease as non-Type-A's, even if they had no other risk factors. This led me to believe that there might be a number of other psychological factors which contribute to the development of heart disease.

Pioneering work by Hans Selye showed that the human body is programmed to respond in specific ways (alarm reactions) to outside stresses, like attacks from animals, physical danger, etc.. The term "fight or flight" was coined to describe this response. Later psychological work has shown that these same responses— adrenaline increase, changes in blood flow to extremities, elevated heart rate, cessation of digestion, increased awareness—can be provoked by psychological factors as well as by physical danger. In other words, people who are prone to fight or flight- Type-A's, for example- maintain a fight-or-flight behavior pattern, with all of the attendant responses, at inappropriate times. These people are ready for war even when there is no call to arms. Their state of chronic readiness leads to vulnerability and lowered bodily resistance, which enhances the probability of disease.. This hypothesis is based on the notion that in each of us there is an area of bodily vulnerability, similar to a weak link in a bicycle chain. After repeated stress, this weakest link will break. For some people, this might mean backaches, for others kidney problems, for others liver ailments, and for people like you and me, heart disease. Maybe there's not much that can be done about our genetic predisposition, but a great deal can be done about the environmental or psychological circumstances that might trigger the specific disease. And that's what we're going to learn.

Once I recovered from surgery, I set out to use my psychological training to determine if there was anything in my own psychological makeup that had contributed to my condition. I did not want to go through by-pass surgery a second time, as is necessary for so many heart patients. It occurred to me that my father and I may have had more in common than by-pass surgery. Since we both thought about things, reacted to events, and interacted with others in strikingly similar ways, perhaps these psychological factors were every bit as important as heredity in the development of heart disease. I reasoned that if this was true, I had more of a chance of making a difference in the progression of my condition. I could change myself, once I identified and examined whatever harmful attitudes and behaviors that both my father and I shared. These similarities are discussed in Chapter 3.

Suppose you conducted a rather strange scientific experiment: dropping a frog into very hot water. The frog, of course would jump out immediately. Now drop a frog into cool water, and gradually heat it. Surprisingly, you would find that the frog would not notice the slow build-up of heat and would not jump out of the boiling pot. The premise of *A Change of Heart* is that heart disease occurs in people with an underlying pre-disposition, a "weak link", who face certain difficult experiences in childhood. *A Change of Heart* regards the heart not just as a mechanical pump, but as a feeling organ connected to the brain and highly responsive to human emotions. Our common expressions, "My heart broke into a thousand pieces", "She broke my heart", or "My heart shrank with fear", highlight this connection. A child may repeatedly endure heart-wrenching experiences, yet be unaware of the gradual damage being done to his heart.

A child who is often emotionally hurt may become depressed without knowing it. First, our nervous system, like that of the frog, responds only to dramatic or abrupt changes in the environment, not to the routine treatment we receive day in and day out while growing up. If you are criticized on a regular basis, you hardly notice your own sighs and heavy-hearted feeling after a while.

Depression in childhood is one of the most under-diagnosed groups of illness in psychiatry. Children are not always able to express how they feel, and the symptoms of depression in childhood take on different forms than in adults. While it may be easy to identify a depressed adult by his verbal statements, lethargic manner or sad expression, depressed children show very different signs. They are more likely to behave in a disruptive or aggressive manner, or to display academic difficulties when they are depressed, thereby masking their depression. Thus, if you ask an adult heart patient whether he experienced depression as a child, he may not be aware that some of his childhood behaviors were symptomatic of depression.

My years in grade school were characterized by fighting with other children to determine "the toughest kid in school", placement in the slow reading group for several years, and frequent absences from school because of stomach cramps. I was not aware that the kinds of symptoms described above were signs of depression, nor were any of the adults in my world. As an adult looking back over my childhood, I know now that I was further hindered by defensive feelings such as denial (no one wants to think of his or her childhood in terms of depression). Also, feelings of loyalty towards my parents made it difficult to get in touch with aspects of their parenting which contributed to my childhood depression. Thus, heart patients may have actually experienced ongoing circumstances which could be labeled traumatic, abusive or depressing, and might be completely out of touch with those experiences.

It has been said that "unhappiness" is the greatest single risk factor for heart disease. And there is ample scientific evidence to support the fact that depression increases the risk of heart attack in adults. It seems likely that for a significant number of adults, the origins of depression can be found in childhood, as was mentioned earlier. These concepts will be discussed further in Chapter 9.

When I was a child, my mother was forced to work in order to support the family, since my father was frequently hospitalized for a number of serious medical problems. This left me without a father for long periods of time, and with a mother who had to raise two children, work full time, pay the bills, and care for a critically ill husband. It was unlikely that any child would get a sense of security, predictability, and unconditional, boundless love from such a background. And in fact I remember my childhood filled with nightmares, heartache, fear and stomach cramps. I hated school, and used to spend hours in the bathroom rather than in class, so upset was I about my life. I developed negative patterns of thinking, believing, and behaving, which set the stage for further damage to my heart. I believed that no one could really like me if they knew me, and that people would take advantage of me if they could, so I behaved as if I were a "tough guy", trying to intimidate others before they intimidated me.

Later I learned to handle the overwhelming anxiety of early childhood by becoming addicted to achievement, performance and accumulation of material possessions. At some point in my life I decided that the only way I could be happy was to become a millionaire. All my efforts went into obtaining this goal. My chest pain began soon after I retired. I felt that I was no longer being productive or useful and this triggered painful memories of earlier failure experiences. For example, I remembered several times when I was suspended from school, failing many courses, and in trouble with the police for minor vandalism. These painful memories pierced through the protective cover of my addiction to achievement.

Life often throws curve balls to parents which sometimes affects their ability to parent. For example, things might be going quite well, when suddenly, the father is laid off from work. Or perhaps, the mother experiences the death of her own parent which throws her off kilter. Parents may go through a separation or divorce which can be traumatic to both partners. In my case, things were going well at home for my parents until my father was called into the Navy where he became disabled. Any of these experiences can impact the parent to the degree that his or her effectiveness as a parent may be compromised.

A frequent result of these kinds of unfortunate experiences is that the child may be an inadvertent victim—lonely and craving attention for long periods of time while the parents deal with the circumstances thrown their way. The child may suffer repeated attacks to his heart as a result of the parents' inability to offer consistent, loving attention and nurturing while attempting to cope with the difficult circumstance. Frequent "corrections" of the child's behavior may occur, as the parent has little tolerance for "misbehavior" while his or her nerves are on edge. An emphasis upon the child's performance may be stressed at this difficult time as well. The child's natural reaction to all this is to learn to value himself conditionally, based upon what he has accomplished, or how he has behaved. His essential self is short-circuited. He learns to react to other people's opinions, beliefs, and admonitions. In the process, he loses touch with his ability to create each moment anew. He spends too much time in his mind, and not enough time in his senses.

A predictable pattern of thinking errors results from this set of experiences. The child learns to think in terms of what he "should" be doing instead of what he may "want" to do. Lacking broad-based experience, the child may jump to conclusions too quickly or over-generalize based upon his limited point of view. His thinking may take on a "black or white" character in which, for example, things may always seem to be certain ways, when the reality may be that things only occasionally are that way. I still find myself thinking that one bad experience means that all similar experiences must turn out bad.

Being raised in a situation where emphasis was placed upon my behavior (as opposed to being loved for just being myself) also had an effect on my self-image. I developed a core belief that I was inadequate or unlovable in some way. I learned to recognize three distinct strategies that I used to deal with this false belief. On occasion, I seemed to *surrender* to my core belief (that is, accept it as true), and this often led to depression, underachievement, and a feeling of being unappreciated or victimized. I would feel sorry for myself if someone didn't pay attention to me, for example. At times I would attempt to *escape* from the sting of the core belief by denial, avoidance or isolation. If I could stay away from people, not get too close, then they would never find out how truly "worthless" I was. And, if I just did those things that I was fairly good at, and stayed away from anything new, then perhaps I could "hide" my felt inadequacies.

But this strategy subjected me to repeated bouts of anxiety as I attempted to ward off anything that could remind me of my perceived failings. Finally, I adopted the strategy of *counterattack*, where I would "prove" to myself and others that I was a force to be reckoned with. In an impatient, arrogant and controlling manner, I would produce as much as possible in the shortest period of time. But even this strategy was flawed, because I would become fearful that I might not have done enough, prepared enough, or considered all the contingencies, and I would be angry when things did not go the way I felt they "should". These strategies are amplified in Chapter 8.

These patterns of defense, formed in childhood to protect against feelings of deficiency, also lead to predictable patterns of interpersonal relationships. The individual who surrenders to a belief of inadequacy, may attract as an adult, people who may attempt to take care of him but somehow never seem to do enough to satisfy him. In my first marriage, my wife was unable to show me the "proper" degree of nurturing and support.

The individual who attempts to escape from his erroneous belief about himself, may have a series of unsatisfactory relationships resulting in his often being alone. I was hard to get close to, and consequently was not invited to many places like my other friends. The <u>counterattacking</u> individual may attract a person who eventually grows tired of being dominated. My second wife made it very clear that she didn't appreciate being treated like the "help". Of course, having used all of these strategies, I led a life where intimacy was often compromised and in which I often abused myself with over-eating and over-work. And, it is the premise of this book that these strategies loaded the deck in favor of developing heart disease.

For example, I was puzzled by my tendency to overeat. I rationalized that I could eat as much as I wanted as long as the foods were "non-fattening". Incredibly, it took only six weeks from the date of my by-pass operation for me to resume my bad eating habits. After some intense soul-searching, I realized that all three strategies described above were operative when it came to bingeing on food. I was attempting to escape a particular situation that was emotionally upsetting to me by "zoning out" with food and denying the possible consequences. At the same time I was counterattacking my core belief of deficiency by defiantly taking in as much food as possible in the shortest period of time, and finally, I was surrendering to my core belief of worthlessness by self-abusive behaviors.

In order to undo this kind of damaging behavior pattern, a person must first become aware of the unconscious strategies he is using, who he is being at any given moment I found that I was being a hard-hearted person in order to protect myself from pain. Only recently have I begun to understand that who I was being was not conducive to health and was not who I really am.

"BEING" AS A FUNCTION OF YOUR SOUL

One can distinguish three domains of human existence; being, doing and having.

<u>Being</u>	<u>Doing</u>	<u>Having</u>
natural	job	possessions
creative	parent role	memories
open	actions	health/illness
intuitive	behaviors	knowledge
spiritual	spouse role	results

We are not accustomed in our culture to recognizing our state of being as an important component of who we are. The dictionary defines "being" as "one's fundamental nature", as in "She responds to music with her whole being." A number of authors equate "being" with the operations of the soul, that higher part of us which whispers to the mind its heartfelt desires. When people are unaware of "being" as a fundamental part of who they are, they simply operate out of "doing" and "having" without consideration of who they are being.

For example, I can be writing this passage with the idea that patients need my expert advice to live. Or rather, that individuals with heart disease have the capacity to heal themselves. Who I am being, where I am coming from, is the work of the soul and will affect the kind of writing I produce and ultimately the results that I may have.

A heart patient can be thought of as a person who essentially concerns himself with "doing" and "having". This orientation is one of production and accumulation of possessions. The individual operates in the sequence have-do-be. For example, this individual may have a certain point of view ("I must constantly work hard") which shapes what he does in life ("I work seventy hour weeks and I never take a vacation") and prevents him from fully experiencing himself as a creative being. This sequence is just the reverse of what works best for health and well-being. Once the heart patient learns to identify and operate from who he really is ("being"), he is in a position to achieve his heartfelt desires ("doing"). He may then accomplish ("have") what he wishes simply as a result of being who he naturally is.

Our culture emphasizes "doing" and "having" perhaps because it is easiest to measure and quantify. Two people can be working side by side turning out an identical number of widgets but they may differ greatly in where they are coming from ("being"). One may truly enjoy his work as a creative outlet while the other may see it as a necessary and painful way of making money so that he can enjoy living after his 8 hours of work. Although I had attained a Ph.D. in psychology, I felt that I needed a year of post-doctoral training at the world-renowned Menninger Foundation in order to prove to myself and others that I was intelligent. I later became wealthy after selling my managed health care company, and yet still felt that I had not accomplished enough. I was laboring under the mistaken belief that doing more or obtaining more possessions would lead to happiness. I learned that true happiness comes only from being who you are.

Honest reflection allowed for a change in my eating habits, as well as an opening of my heart to more meaningful relationships, the ability to escape from some of the distorting, constricted, erroneous beliefs of my cultural world view, and increased access to my authentic and spiritual self. *A Change of Heart* is the result of my learning to face difficult emotions that were long denied, and to get in touch with the thinking patterns and belief system that dictated the course of my life for too many years.

You too can become acquainted with your essential nature, and learn to recognize when you are operating from your cultural identity and when you are being who you naturally are. This distinction makes all the difference when it comes to sticking to stated goals.

For example, if you are keeping the lawn mowed primarily because you are concerned with what the neighbors might think, you may approach the task differently from the way you would if took pleasure in creating a beautiful yard. In the first case, you may feel resentful of and burdened by the task; in the second you may actually enjoy the work. It is more likely that the lawn will be mowed if the act is an expression of who you are.

In order to express yourself fully, you will need to become acquainted with aspects of yourself that may have been suppressed for a long time. Before this is possible, however, you will need to discover what it is that covers over your essential nature. The next two chapters set the stage for this process to begin. Chapter 4 discusses the secretly- sensitive personality structure of the heart patient which keeps us from experiencing our true potential. Chapters 5, 6, 7, and 8 explain how certain thoughts and beliefs can rob us of joy, aliveness, and the natural expression of our deepest selves. Chapter 9 expands upon and amplifies the ideas in Chapter 4. Chapters 10 and 11 will introduce you to your capacity for pure creativity, your unlimited potential and the incredible power within you.

CHAPTER 2

STARTING FROM WHERE YOU ARE

A journey of a thousand miles begins with one step.
Anonymous

It has been said that the way to anywhere is to start from where you are. Of course there are those people, like myself, who feel that starting from scratch is too slow, or boring. I often leaf through a book, skip to the end of each chapter or the summaries in order not to "waste my time". If you are this way, I urge you to read this book in a more conventional way. This is because each chapter builds on the preceding one, and later chapters may seem confusing without the grounding that comes earlier.

Take a minute to ask yourself how your heart disease happened. Was it the result of heredity? Did you develop heart disease because of poor eating habits? Was it a lack of exercise that caused your condition? Perhaps your heart disease was the result of years of stress, or some combination of the above? Or was it merely "fate"?

Try to remember how you felt when you learned that you had heart disease. Were you frightened? Did you attempt to minimize the seriousness of your condition? Were you angry?

Now take another minute or two to get in touch with some of the things that you have tried to do to combat your disease. Did you go on a diet or start an exercise program? Did you start a regime of medication? Have you enrolled in a rehabilitation program?

If you are like many of the heart patients I have seen, you were quite upset at learning that you had heart disease, and had good intentions of making the changes in your life that your doctors recommended. You may have felt victimized by your condition, as if fate was being cruel to you. You may have decided that you were going to fight this unfair condition.

Several years ago I learned that I had the beginning stages of heart disease. I was shocked at first, but soon began to deny or minimize the seriousness of my condition. I reasoned that I had discovered my condition early enough to do something about it. But after a few weeks of eating the right foods, and increasing my exercise program, I slowly began to resume my old ways. I was not plagued by painful symptoms which might remind me to stick to a healthy lifestyle. My disease took on a slow, almost invisible progression, making it easy for me to deny what was going on. By the time symptoms appeared, in the form of a constricted feeling in my chest, I was a candidate for quadruple by-pass surgery. Perhaps you could tell a similar story.

What was going on with me that could allow for such an outcome? Are heart patients more self-destructive than other people? Unconscious? Stupid? What kind of thought patterns would support this kind of behavior? Why was I resisting what I knew would be good for me? Who was I being with respect to my heart disease, and could I be someone else who was more effective?

Even after by-pass surgery, I found myself resuming some of the bad habits I had before, reasoning that I was now on medication which would prevent plaque from forming in my new arteries, and that even if the medication didn't help, I could always undergo surgery again in ten years or so. How remarkable it is that I could forget the pain of surgery so soon! It didn't help that I was a psychologist. I was still blind to my rationalizations.

HEART PATIENTS ARE TOUGH CUSTOMERS

I shared many of the characteristics of the heart patients in the group therapy program for heart patients that I led. We were mostly educated, professional people. Many of us had a great sense of humor, and a capacity for caring. We enjoyed each other's company for the most part. But where we seemed to differ in personality make-up was in the area of what is called "psychological-mindedness". For the most part the group members were not interested in the deeper aspects of what made them tick. In fact, many harbored deep-seated doubts about the whole field of psychology, and especially the idea that somehow they might have had a hand in their illness, and further, that they could have a hand in helping themselves to survive it, and prevail over it. They were a bunch of tough customers.

They wanted concrete examples of what I was saying. They were concerned about how useful or practical my input was. "What you said Dr. Decker was all very nice, but how does that impact on my life?", was a refrain I heard any time I would wax poetic or philosophical. If I sought to get underneath their behavior to deeper motivations, I was often met with a blank stare or "There you go again, Dr. Decker, with your psychologizing". They were much more comfortable with the relaxation exercises or the parts of the program where information about diet, exercise or cardiology was discussed. They wanted to be told what to do. They did not want to spend time understanding themselves. After all, it is far easier to recognize and deal with external causes for our heart disease than to look deep within ourselves and find things which make us uncomfortable.

WHAT MAKES SOME HEART PATIENTS SO TOUGH?

Many heart patients have certain things in common. Among other things, many have had to deal with difficult situations which hardened them and helped them to survive. Perhaps some of what follows will seem familiar to you. When I was a child, I was often alone, so I had to became independent. I became competitive in order to prove to myself and others that I was a somebody. School was difficult for me, but I forced myself to learn because information was a form of power and a source of protection for me. I became cynical, after repeated disappointments in my early life. And I was depressed or angry a good deal of the time because I was not able to receive the kind of nurturing and love at home that I needed. Of course, I had no time, during the earlier years to analyze my motivations—I was too busy trying to survive.

When I was in practice as a clinical psychologist, there were some kinds of patients that I loved to see because they were easy to work with and made rapid progress. Others were less enjoyable to work with only because progress was so difficult. People who came in the door as a result of a difficult situation were relatively easy to treat. For example, a woman who had been functioning well for many years, sought help after her husband left her. This "adjustment reaction" responded well to a few sessions of psychotherapy. So called "neurotic" individuals were a little more difficult. These people struggled with long-standing feelings of anxiety or depression as a result of some hidden inner conflicts. For example, a patient became anxious every time she ate in a restaurant. She was unconsciously afraid that she would do something wrong and make a fool of herself.

The patients who were most difficult to treat, were those with so-called "personality disorders". These individuals rarely experienced symptoms like depression or anxiety, because there was little in the way of internal conflict. Most of the time, they showed up at my office against their will, referred by a demanding spouse, parent or judge. Their only conflicts appeared to be with other people who seemed to make too many demands, or lack understanding. Rarely did they take responsibility for anything in their lives. It was always someone else's fault. Though heart patients do not generally have personality disorders, I believe that they are at least as tough as these individuals, probably even tougher, in a way. This is because the presence of physical symptoms on top of personality characteristics, suggests that there were many instances in the past where "warnings" from the body went unheeded, much as the patient fails to hear messages from those around him, messages which could have helped to prevent or mitigate his or her later illness. I came to believe that heart patients develop a hard-hearted, though secretly-sensitive, approach to life which makes them tough customers.

When I went into therapy with my first wife in an effort to save my marriage, I was not a good patient. There was little that the therapist could tell me that I didn't already know. I wasn't very anxious because I "knew" that the problem with my marriage was my wife, not myself. Change wives, and all would be better, I reasoned. Only when the same problems began to crop up in my second marriage did it dawn on me that perhaps I had something to do with the problems.

Do you find that you too are a "tough customer" when it comes to trying to understand your deeper self? Are you more interested in facts, data, and what is immediately practical and useful? Would you rather that your doctor just come right out and *tell* you what to do, and cut out all the warm and fuzzy stuff? Do you have a "tough hide" that is hard to penetrate?

SHORT TERM GROUP PROGRAMS FOR HEART PATIENTS- WHY THEY DON'T WORK FOR US

The problem is that the approach which might feel the most comfortable, probably won't work. The members of my group learned a great deal about diet, exercise, medication and the workings of the heart, but most of them were still 25 or more pounds overweight at the end of the ten-week program. Those that drank too much or smoked cigarettes, continued to do so. Several patients were re-hospitalized during the program. A recent study indicated that the kind of program that I was conducting had little chance of success. D.A. Jones conducted a seven-session outpatient program with heart patients from six general hospitals in Wales. The objectives of the program were to provide patients with information about heart disease, and recovery from myocardial infarction, to increase patient awareness about stress and stressful situations, to teach relaxation skills, to improve responses to stressful situations and develop coping skills' to promote positive adjustment to illness, and to rebuild confidence in patients and spouses. (All this within 14 hours). The results indicated that there were no differences between the people who went through the program and those who didn't.

Based upon my experience leading a group of heart patients, the results of studies like the one mentioned above, my experiences with individual psychotherapy patients, and my own experience, (with both my father's illness and my own reality as a difficult heart patient), I can say with confidence that the heart patient is a tough customer. He or she will take in all kinds of information, but do little in the long run to put that information to good use.

It is not enough to provide the heart patient with information about risk factors. Nor is it sufficient to teach the heart patient how to change his behavior. This is because, he will change back sooner or later. I have found that it takes a fundamental shift in who the heart patient *is being* in order for desired changes to stick. This involves an exploration through territory that is particularly difficult for the heart patient to enter—namely his own psychological make-up.

Why We're Here

I am convinced that people have it within themselves to take this journey. You would not have bought this book unless you had the desire and courage to make the kinds of fundamental changes that you deem necessary for your health and well-being. Remember that I share your journey. I, too, have heart disease. I, too, have had to face painful realities of life and death. And I have chosen life. You can too.

CHAPTER 3

OPENING YOURSELF TO CHANGE

The head learns new things, but the heart forever
practices old experiences.
Henry Ward Beecher

Of all the words in the English language, "change" seems the most threatening to me. This would appear surprising, since I suppose that nearly everyone likes to experience new things from time to time. After all, eating the same dinner every night can get boring. And what would life be like if every day were the same as the day before? My wife periodically raids my closet, throws out clothing that I just know will come back in style some day, and forces me to buy new clothes. I believe that there is a significant part of me that welcomes sameness, even at the expense of novelty, growth, or even marital peace. I have been known to eat the same thing for lunch every day, and to make a religion out of habit and routine. God help those who try to interfere with my rituals in the morning. Let me have my coffee before attempting to engage me in conversation of any kind. I remember that my father was the same way. We would dine at the same restaurants, travel to the same places and repeat the most ridiculous jokes over and over again.

This is not to say that neither one of us would ever try anything new. My father was a courageous man in many respects-- starting college very late in life despite his disability--and I fancy myself as equally game in several areas. For example, I have taken many risks in my personal and professional life, most of them with positive outcomes. I married a second time, and started a managed healthcare business by accepting monetary risk. Even so, my wife has to force me to go to new places or experience new things, though once the kicking and screaming subsides, I usually find that I am enjoying myself.

The goal of this book is to introduce you to valuable aspects of yourself that have been long suppressed, and consequently are unavailable for healing. When I set out to achieve this goal for myself, I discovered that there was something standing in my way; namely my old patterns of thinking and believing and a misidentification of myself with these patterns of thinking and believing. For me to get to the point where these patterns of thought and belief could be explored, a formidable obstacle had to be overcome. The obstacle I am talking about is the very human tendency to prefer things just the way they are, to avoid rocking the boat for fear of falling out. I had become so accustomed to and attached to my ways of being, that it was difficult to allow new and possibly contradictory information to come in, even if this information could save my life. I saw that this "resistance" to change operates at an unconscious level, and therefore had to be exposed to the light of day in order for a change of heart to occur. From my experience as a psychologist, I knew that this "resistance" was not peculiar to me, but was present in all people to varying degrees, and had to be dealt with as a first order of business.

WHY IT IS SO DIFFICULT TO CHANGE

You have probably heard the expression that people prefer the "devil they know, to the devil they don't". What this means to me is that we are more comfortable with familiar situations and circumstances than with new ones. New situations are untested and unpredictable, therefore more risky, and stressful. Thus, even miserable conditions have some redeeming value in that they are at least familiar. This may explain why many people who are in marriages that are abusive and unsatisfying continue to endure injustices. These people may reason that it is better to be in a known circumstance, with all the negatives, than risk having a potentially worse set of circumstances which could come with change. Shakespeare's Hamlet spoke of "bearing the ills we have" rather than "fly to others we know not of..." Heart patients have a similar vested interest in what is known and familiar. It could be argued that we have an even stronger need for consistency than others.

In my background, for example, there was a good deal of family insecurity. We were financially strapped, without a father for long periods of time, and always anxious about his medical condition. I believe that heart patients in general, have experienced more loss and insecurity than is found in the general population. I base this belief, in part on recent research that indicates that depression in the twenties commonly precedes heart disease in the forties. Since there is also evidence that the behaviors of three-year-olds can predict depression in the twenties, it stands to reason that depressed twenty year olds could have been depressed much earlier.

What kind of family circumstances would lead to depression in children as young as three? A family atmosphere that lacked predictability, security, and love would be likely to foster depression among other traits. In fact, there is longitudinal evidence that pre-adolescents whose primary disorder is depression continue having depressive episodes in adolescence, and studies of parent ratings have identified a clear-cut syndrome of problems in children from four to eleven years old, including unhappiness, sadness, feelings of worthlessness and inferiority. Another investigator found that early onset depression tends to continue into adulthood. In a study conducted in Germany emphasizing sociological and psychological variables, middle class, first and last-born persons, children of elderly mothers and those of large families were prone to heart disease. Such families were found to be unstable with regard to role, status and position. Additional pre-disposing factors are job dissatisfaction, loss and recurring stress situations. Finally, in a study conducted in Egypt the prevalence of heart disease in schoolchildren was highest in illiterate families with unskilled fathers, high crowding, and low socio-economic status.

For many of the reasons outlined above, the status quo is often a sought after and longed for goal. Even our nervous systems seem to prefer what is familiar and routine, often reacting with alarm when things seem unusual or out of place. I have two sheltie dogs that seem to become hysterical whenever the wind blows, or an unfamiliar sound is heard. Humans and animals alike, seem to accommodate to circumstances, however poisonous or noxious. We put up with polluted air, dirty rivers and streams, poverty and even abuse as long as there is a gradual buildup rather than a sudden event.

I was unaware that my early family situation was unusual or that I was not getting what children in intact or secure families were able to get in the way of predictability, love and attention. If my father had died, or I had become a ward of the state, I would have noticed these sudden and dramatic changes more easily.

There is another reason why it is difficult to change. People are so addicted to "being right" that it is almost as if they would rather be right than be happy or even alive. If you have chosen a particular path in life, or hold a particular belief dearly, you will be reluctant to give up that belief. Religious wars are often fought because each side is highly invested in the "rightness" of their beliefs. A prisoner of war may prefer to die, rather than adopt beliefs that he considers to be wrong.

On a less serious note, I remember my college buddy complaining about his father one day. It seemed that my friend, George, was arguing that a particular medical problem was the result of certain conditions, a contention sorely debated by his uninformed father. When George presented his father with a medical source book, his father dismissed the book as inaccurate, rather than admit that he could be wrong.

When I argue with my wife about the meaningless stuff that couples argue about, both of us fall into the trap of needing to be right, which of course makes the other wrong. Since no one likes to be wrong, the fight continues until one of us finally walks away. On a good day, I can interrupt this kind of banter by recognizing that the conversation goes nowhere as long as I am attacking my wife by making her wrong. I try to see her point, and at least let her know that I understand it, even if I don't agree with it. Just being understood seems to go a long way towards mending fences.

Suppose that you have taken a major position with respect to your belief about how something should be done. Would you rather be right with respect to your position, at the expense of your relationship, or would you value harmony in your relationship at the expense of being right? Many people would opt for being right over the well-being of their relationships. "My wife should prepare meals only with low fat ingredients, and when she doesn't she is simply wrong." This statement could make for a wonderful argument, with no clear winner. Hard feelings will most likely come about, making it less likely that the husband will ever get what he wants. Perhaps one would have a better chance at a positive outcome if he said something like "I appreciate it that you work so hard in preparing my meals, and that for the most part they are low-fat. It is hard for me to resist those foods that are not low fat, and would appreciate your help".

RESISTING CHANGE

Resistance is a term often used by psychologists to account for why a patient might not have complied with the doctor's recommendations. For example, if the patient is asked to invite his spouse with him to the next session, and the patient shows up without his spouse, he may be thought to be "resistant". Now the patient may protest that there are perfectly good reasons for his "forgetting" to invite the spouse. He was very busy that week. His wife was ill. The phases of the moon were out of sync. But deep down, the psychologist will know, and the patient will sense that there is more going on. But resistance is by definition an unconscious process, so that the psychologist will typically explore with the patient some of the hidden reasons why he may have forgotten.

Resistance, then, is an unconscious attempt to avoid compliance. People resist for a variety of reasons. Some may attempt to preserve a tenuous sense of self-esteem. For example, if you need to be right all the time, it may be because your self-image is weak. Some individuals resist as an expression of anger, as for example "I'm going to dig in my heels because she keeps bugging me". People also resist because change frightens them, preferring the "devil" they know or the status quo, as mentioned earlier. Perhaps the person above "forgot" to remind his wife to accompany him because he was afraid of what she might say to the psychologist. This could be an unconscious effort to preserve self-esteem or an effort to avoid having to make changes repeatedly requested by his wife. If the patient had been angry at the doctor, but unable to express his anger directly, he might have unconsciously expressed the anger by failing to comply with the doctor's request. If the doctor confronted the patient, by saying "I think that you may have been angry at me and that is why you forgot", the patient might deny that he was angry.

Resistance is often reinforced by "secondary gain". For example, by not complying with doctors' orders, a number of seemingly positive things could happen to the individual. The patient might enjoy the attention he gets from loved ones who rush to admonish him whenever he "forgets" to take his medications. Or by failing to do what was requested, the patient may require others to do for him, thereby getting himself out of undesirable work.

There even may be a subtle form of pressure brought to bear by caretakers for the patient to remain non-compliant. In these cases, the patient senses that the caretaker would be "out of a job" if the patient complied with recommendations and health dramatically improved.

Denial is an unconscious form of resistance marked by a tendency towards wishful thinking. For example you may wish that it really doesn't matter whether you take your medicine or don't. Or as above, the patient may wish that he had not been angry because he associated anger with being "bad" or disloyal. After all, he may reason, "My doctor is only trying to do what is best for me, and therefore I shouldn't get angry at him." The patient, because of somewhat harsh early training, may not recognize the legitimacy of his own anger.

I was one of the most resistant people around. Perhaps because of authority conflicts or passive-aggressiveness, I used to go so far as to take up two parking spaces just because I refused to be limited by the lines. I would frequently do the opposite of what I was told to do. These tendencies were bad enough when it came to getting along with others. The problem was compounded when it spilled over into areas affecting my health. Thus when my doctor suggested certain medications or life-style adjustments, not complying with his advice would often lead to negative consequences to my health.

Non-compliance with recommended medical advice is not a problem unique to me. The problem costs insurance companies and health care providers millions of dollars a year, to say nothing of the costs in terms of human suffering and workplace absenteeism. Drug companies would spend a fortune if they knew how to get patients with high blood pressure to consistently take their medicine. Despite a mushrooming of programs developed by these companies to educate patients about the benefits of consistent patterns of behavior, many patients "forget" their medications. And of course, we all know how successful we have been following our doctor's advice to lose weight or give up smoking or drinking.

On the surface it is puzzling why we should be non-compliant when it comes to following good advice, particularly when our health is on the line. Looking at compliance more carefully, offers some insight.

Compliance can be defined as cooperation with the wishes of an external authority. For example, your doctor or boss requests that you do something and you acquiesce. But if you look more closely, there is a hidden degree of resistance built into compliance, which explains why so many individuals who seemingly comply with doctors' orders, eventually "forget" everything they were told to do. The bottom line is that many people hate to be told what to do.

A number of people will comply with directions because they are afraid of the consequences of non-compliance. For example, a child will sit perfectly still as requested, if he senses that his life or allowance is on the line. But remove the threat, and the child's incentive for compliance goes with it. As soon as the parent turns his back, the child is off the wall again. The chances are improved for the child eventually to sit still if he comes to his own conclusion that sitting still is a good thing. He may recognize that by sitting still he seems to learn more, or to get more positive attention. Compliance with external authority stands in marked contrast to adherence with goals you have taken to be your own.

Adherence can be thought of as an internal decision to stick to certain recommendations based on your own desires. For example, you may decide that avoiding sugar, as recommended by your doctor, is a good idea, and adopt that idea as your own. *Adherence has a much better chance of succeeding than compliance because of its internal locus of control.* Adherence implies that you are calling the shots. If you fail to adhere to your own set of expectations, you might feel disappointed in yourself, and try harder. But you probably would not feel guilty or fearful, as might be the case when you fail to comply, or even secretly satisfied if you managed to ventilate your anger by frustrating those who "demanded" compliance.

It is this author's opinion that heart patients are highly-resistant individuals, despite surface behaviors to the contrary. Many of the patients in my heart group were genuinely puzzled by their inability to lose weight or stop drinking. This is because resistance is an unconscious process, operating by definition outside their awareness. The source of their resistance may lie in their childhood experiences. Many heart patients experience a lack of unconditional positive regard. They learn to value themselves based on their performance, not on who they are. At a deep level these individuals become resentful of the conditions attached to receiving loving attention. They comply, but with a heavy heart. They sense that their essential selves are given little acknowledgment, and they are resentful. Thus compliance with authority becomes a double-edged sword. Compliance becomes necessary for approval. But anger and resistance are generated by the deep understanding that loving attention is conditional.

HOW TO RECOGNIZE WHEN YOU ARE RESISTANT TO CHANGE

- Do you find yourself on a regular basis "forgetting " to do what was recommended, such as taking your medications, or avoiding sweets?
- Do you catch yourself frequently having thoughts such as "nobody can tell me what to do" or "no one can help me"?
- Are you frequently puzzled as to why you don't follow advice that you know would be good for you?
- If you were brutally honest with yourself, would you agree that a part of you enjoys frustrating those who care about you?
- Do you get out of doing things that you don't enjoy simply by remaining sick?
- Are you afraid to change, and thereby take comfort in doing the same damaging things over and over again?
- Do you feel a certain degree of pressure to remain sick because you sense that a loved one needs to feel needed?

If you found yourself agreeing with a number of these items, there is a good chance that you are harboring some unconscious resistance.

SOURCES OF MOTIVATION TO OVERCOME RESISTANCE TO CHANGE

There are a number of ways that you can train yourself to become more open and less resistant. Of course, just recognizing that you may be resistant to new ideas is a major first step. Many people go through their lives with rigid beliefs about how things should be done, and no clue about the possibility of seeing things from other points of view. Once you have taken the step to look honestly at yourself, unconscious resistance has nowhere to hide.

Pain and dissatisfaction are strong motivators. Try to recognize that whatever gain you are getting from resisting or non-compliance, the cost to you in terms of suffering is not worth the price.

Recognize that change is a process that takes time and is rarely smooth.   You need to be ready to change, and willing to pick yourself up after several failures. A popular commercial, "Just do it!", does not really take into consideration the fact that people usually change by fits and starts, rather than willpower. Action usually occurs after a person has prepared himself for change, perhaps by recognizing the need , developing a plan, or by making his or her intended changes public.

Your ideal image can be a powerful source of motivation. Try to visualize yourself healthy and vital. Keep that image in mind the next time you are non-compliant.

External reinforcement is a powerful motivator. Set up an agreement with loved ones to reward you for behaviors in keeping with your ideal self. For example, you may ask for a hug each time that you compliment or praise a family member.

Hope and optimism are two sources of motivation. To the degree that you have a positive attitude towards what is possible for you, you improve the chances of directing your behavior towards healthy outcomes.

Success is always rewarding. Get in touch with your successes and celebrate them. Nothing is more reinforcing than dwelling on the previous behaviors that led to success.

Adherence is a positive word to add to your vocabulary. Get in touch with your heart-felt desires, and adhere to those behaviors that lead to your own goals.

Take tiny steps. Achieving goals through small incremental steps makes it more likely that you will not frighten yourself with the enormity of your self appointed tasks. It is much easier to learn to dive from the edge of the pool, before you tackle the diving board.

CHANGE AS A SOURCE OF STRESS

Stress can be a killer, according to just about any magazine that you pick up today. For our purposes, stress is defined as anything that overpowers your abilities to cope. When you are in a situation that demands more from you than your resources can handle, you will experience stress. Obviously this broad definition allows for great variability, since different people have different resources to bring to bear in a given situation. Thus what may be stressful to me, may not be for you. For example, I would nearly panic at the thought of having to fix a flat tire, while for you it may be a mere inconvenience.

All of us are bombarded daily with changes that can become potential stressors. Many of us can be overwhelmed by traffic shifts, unpredictable weather, sudden noise, unwanted pollution, or other environmental events. Deadlines, financial pressures, demands for time and attention, losses of family members, are some of the social events that may require changes in the way that you behave. Aging, accidents, disease, and the inability to exercise or to sleep are some of the unwelcome physiological events that can also lead to feelings of stress.

But in modern times, the greatest source of stress seems to be internal, in the form of disturbing patterns of thought. Most of us are not struggling to cut wood to keep our families warm, or fending off wild animals to protect our children. We have the time to dwell on the bothersome issues of daily life—repairing the fence, taking the children to soccer practice, paying overdue bills. How we think about these mundane events determines the degree to which we feel stressed. For example, if you think that you would be a bad parent if you missed soccer practice, you likely feel pressure to attend. Similarly, if you think that an unsightly fence would damage your relationship to your neighbors, you will experience stress until the situation is remedied.

Stress, then, is dependent upon your appraisal of a given situation. If you don't pay a particular bill, do you see your credit going south, your house repossessed, and yourself in debtor's prison, or do you envision a simple phone call reminding you to pay the bill, and a late fee paid? Your appraisal of the gravity of the non- payment circumstance will determine how stressed you become. Thoughts that disrupt a relatively peaceful state of mind tend to be experienced as stressful.

MENTAL STRESS AND THE HEART

A recent study at Duke University demonstrated that high levels of mental stress, can trigger a drop in the blood supply to the heart, and double the risk of myocardial ischemia, a possibly fatal condition. In another study, researchers from Harvard University showed that worrying about financial, health or social issues increased the risk of heart attack by 20 to 70 percent in a group of 2280 men. It was speculated that people with high levels of anxiety or worry may have a greater tendency to secrete adrenaline, a hormone that raises heart rates.

Whenever you are threatened, your body responds with a "fight or flight" reaction. A series of biochemical changes occurs to help you deal with danger. Your heart rate, breathing rate, muscle tension, metabolism and blood pressure all increase. Hands and feet get cold as blood flows to larger muscles.

It has been suggested that the flow of blood away from organs that are less essential when responding to threat, impedes organs like the liver from processing cholesterol, resulting in the build-up of plaque. When stressors are unrelenting, for example during a major work reorganization, divorce or when coping with chronic illness, the body remains aroused and mobilized for fight or flight, and remains in a chronic state of "fight or flight."

PERSONALITY AND STRESS

People obviously differ as to their personalities. You may know someone who is hard driving and aggressive, while a neighbor may seem to have a sweet and gentle disposition. Do some people have personalities which make it more likely that they will experience stress? The answer is a definite yes. The hard-driving individual may experience stress fairly often as he measures himself against his accomplishments, or regards others in terms of their usefulness in obtaining his goals. Individuals with more passive personalities may be more self-accepting, and less offensive to others, resulting in fewer instances of potentially threatening situations coming their way. In the next chapter, you will be introduced to the personality structure of the heart patient. You will see that he is basically an extremely sensitive individual who hides the softer sides of himself for protection. He is a pussycat with the roar of a tiger. The tiger side of him is "hard-hearted", designed to throw people off the trail of his sensitive nature. People like this experience stress almost all the time. This is because their low self-esteem makes them vulnerable to perceived criticism. They also have thinking patterns which create pressure to perform at impossibly high levels. Finally, their anger often gets in the way of developing close relationships.

You will see in a later chapter that just <u>having</u> a personality can be a source of stress to the degree that it is distinct from the essence of who you are. If I as a psychologist, for example, believe that I should be a certain way—professional, in-control, staid—and I bring that personality to every situation such as a party, or an intimate encounter with a loved one, the discrepancy between who I think I <u>should</u> be and who I might <u>want</u> to be can cause enormous stress. I'm not suggesting that you should not have a personality, but, rather, that your personality should draw on who you <u>really</u> are.

Personalities are developed over time, based on experience and innate disposition, and are reinforced by society. While they may serve a useful purpose in providing a short- hand device for categorizing people, a personality ultimately limits your possibilities for growth and change.

After reading this section, you can see that there are major barriers to change. People have a need for sameness and familiarity that is rooted in their nervous systems. Change therefore can be something to fear, and a source of stress. People need to be "right" about their beliefs, positions, thoughts and manner of being in the world. Anything that contradicts their point of view can be threatening to their self-esteem. People get angry when they are told what to do, even if they sense that compliance would be helpful. We all have strong wishes which sometimes delude us into thinking that there are no repercussions to our negative behaviors. Many of us have hidden conflicts with authority which prevent us from following even good advice, particularly if we feel that it is being jammed down our throats.

For some of us, there may be some unconscious reasons why we prefer to be ill, for example to get out of work or to frustrate others. Thoughts that disrupt our peace of mind can be a source of stress, and affect our hearts in negative ways. Certain personalities generate thought patterns which are more stressful than other personality types.

Change is difficult. There are many reasons why people will maintain the status quo even if kills them. If you can be aware of these tendencies, perhaps you will be more open to what follows in subsequent chapters. You will notice just how attached you are to your thoughts and beliefs, and how resistant you may be to other ways of looking at things, even though your health may depend on it.

CHAPTER 4

THE SECRETLY-SENSITIVE HEART PATIENT:
A PUSSYCAT IN TIGER'S STRIPES

Give all to love. Obey thy heart
Emerson

You saw in the last chapter that in order to figure out what made me tick, I first had to determine the barriers to that very process. I learned that I was addicted to sameness, and therefore I had mixed feelings about looking inside myself. The prospects of discovering that I might have to change did not make me a happy camper. Besides, I took pride in having already figured myself out. After all, I was a psychologist. If anyone should know the landscape of his mind it ought to be me. If I learned something new about myself, I might feel that my previous view of myself was wrong, and I don't like being wrong about anything. Finally, I knew I had wishes about how I wanted to be seen by others, and so perhaps I had the same desires to be seen positively by myself at the end of my search.

With all these potential obstacles to overcome, you can see that trying to figure out your own personality is not easy, even for a psychologist. Of course I reminded myself why I wanted to take this journey. After all, I had heart disease, and I suspected that I might have something to do with that fact, independent of my genetic make-up. In other words, I wanted to understand myself better in order to determine if I was operating in ways that could impact negatively upon my health. By so doing, I hoped that I could effect a positive outcome instead.

So here is what I found. I discovered a number of conflicting characteristics and traits, which on the surface seemed confusing. For example, I knew that my patients often experienced me as warm, caring and generous. Yet I knew in my heart that there were plenty of times when I was selfish, insensitive and detached. The same contradictions showed up when I thought about the group of heart patients that I led. Many of the heart patients in my group had really terrific qualities. Several had great senses of humor. Many of my patients demonstrated politeness, a good work ethic, and a sincere desire to learn about certain aspects of their disease. However, there were also times when these same people seemed cold-hearted, petty, self-centered and hostile.

When I thought about things more, I remembered that my father also had this kind of confusing combination of traits. I smile to myself as I recall him listening to the radio, joyfully singing out loud and waving an imaginary wand as he put the orchestra through its paces. He, too, was beloved by many of his clients. Yet my father could be vindictive, critical, harsh and insensitive.

As I began to look more deeply into my personality structure, I was struck with the fact that my father and I shared many personality characteristics which could be seen as hard-hearted, as if we needed to hide our sensitive and vulnerable sides, to appear tough and formidable. As you already know, both my father and I underwent quadruple by-pass surgery. It seemed to me that the downplaying of our tenderhearted traits, in combination with the emphasis upon our "Kingly" or arrogant personality characteristics might have contributed to our condition. Some of these traits are mentioned below.

Both my father and I were quick to anger. Each one of us was extremely competitive, needing to win at board games, the stock market, or in my case, tennis. And both my father and I appeared to be selfish to others. Neither one of us would go out of our way to please other people. We did what was most convenient for ourselves, unless we were given very good reasons to deviate from this posture. Both of us seemed rigid in our thinking, over-reacted to minor events, and were stingy with time, money and the sharing of warm or positive feelings. We seemed to believe that the display of tender emotions was best left to women. Our social relationships were characterized by long-term relationships with a few good friends. It was very difficult for both of us to establish meaningful relationships with "new" people. We were even similar in our sense of humor. Both of us enjoyed a pun or play on words, often accompanied by groans by anyone within earshot. However our humor was often sarcastic. For example, upon meeting a family we hadn't seen in some time, either my father or I would be known to remark to the parents that their child "grew some" (appeared gruesome). This play on words seemed funny to us, and no one else.

Perhaps this kind of "humor" had more profound effects on my thinking than I know about. I learned to see things in different ways, and eventually to look beneath what was presented on the surface. While this tendency had apparent advantages in terms of solving problems, it also made it less likely that I would accept things as they were. I learned to read into what people were saying and to distrust many of their words. Like my father's, my thinking became somewhat suspicious, distrustful, and even cynical, always looking out for what the person "really meant". This made me less spontaneous in my interactions with others, and made it more difficult to get close to people.

Apparently my father and I also shared similar experiences as children, which left us vulnerable in similar ways. For example, neither one of us grew up in a home with a father who was consistently present, emotionally or physically. In marked contrast to the personalities of my father and myself, stood the personalities of my wife and my mother.

I would sometimes look at my wife or my mother, and wonder what planet they came from. They had personality characteristics which were nothing like my own, or my father's. When they were with people, they were both really there. By this I mean that they were fully engaged with the other person, totally riveted to them, following their every word or feeling with empathy and understanding. Their sensitivities were out there for all to see, not hidden beneath a pile of protective barriers that did more to smother than to protect. When I interact with people, I often have to force myself to remain focused on them. I am thinking about other things, wondering what I am going to say next, how the other person regards me, or what he may "really" want from me. Interacting with my father had many of the same qualities. He might continue reading the paper while engaging in conversation with me. Sometimes, I knew he didn't hear what I was saying, so preoccupied was he with some of his own thoughts.

I am married to a truly wonderful woman. I am not alone in this opinion, as she has a number of very dear friends who also love her deeply, and even people who meet her for the first time remark positively about her. I am not trying to make her out to be a perfect person. She has her share of faults just like most of us. But she really has a number of qualities which I value. My mother had similar positive qualities. My father used to tease my mother about the number of dear friends she had. "Your mother never met a person who wasn't absolutely wonderful, or had a meal which wasn't the most delicious ever," he would remark with a wink. Neither my father, nor I shared the kind of warm personality and optimistic attitude that would attract others.

It seemed obvious that my personality, and that of my father, were not particularly conducive to getting close to people. After all, people were not blind to the fact that they were not getting our full attention. They may have felt slighted or offended by our treatment. In other words, we actively isolated ourselves, and isolation from others has been proven to be a risk factor for illness. This idea will be explored in a later chapter.

My wife and my mother were the social directors of their respective houses. Social relationships were considered "women's work" by both my father and me. Consequently, they were charged with the responsibility of arranging social gatherings, trips with others, vacations, birthday parties, any gifts that were appropriate, cards, phone calls to express concern or condolences—in short any activity that would bring one human being closer to another. There were times when I really wanted to do some of these things myself, like talk to a friend for no apparent reason. But I was afraid to show my sensitive side. I would tell my wife that she was "better at those things" and she would be pressed into duty. I secretly wished that I could talk to others the way that she could, because I wanted to feel the same kind of love and affection that others had for her.

There are many other ways in which my wife and I differ in our surface behaviors. I accuse her of being easily distracted, while extolling my virtues as a focused individual, able to get done what I set out to do despite the distractions. A less pleasant way for me to look at this set of facts, is to recognize that my wife is able to go with the flow at any given moment, being flexible and adaptive to changing circumstances, whereas I tend to be rigid, and goal oriented to the point that I screen out important relationship issues.

My wife is an adventurous person who is always game for new experiences. I have to be pushed into new experiences, because of my fears of disturbing the status quo. I have control only in areas that are known to me, whereas the unknown has risks which seem daunting.

Underlying much of my day-to-day activities, appears to be a kind of sour or slightly-depressive disposition. I am poised to register with anger or irritation any frustration, interruption, inconvenience, or unpredictable event. If the phone rings, and it is for someone else, I will silently sulk. In addition, I will be resentful that I have to interrupt whatever I was doing to find whoever was being asked for by the caller. My father was equally unpleasant. If the newspaper was late, or arrived in less than pristine condition, all hell would break loose in the family. This underlying predisposition is, thankfully, not shared by my wife. Not that she goes about her day humming, or doing cartwheels, but she is generally pleasant to be around, and one doesn't have to fear an explosion around the next corner.

I tend to be selfish with my time or money, while my wife is generous. She is the first to volunteer her efforts to clean-up after a function, whereas I am nowhere to be found. She does all kinds of community work without compensation, but I have a hard time valuing anything, particularly my time, without a price tag. My wife will lend anybody anything, which usually drives me crazy until the items are returned safely. She will spend what seems like inordinate amounts of money on gifts for others, while I rationalize that people should like me just for myself, not the gifts I bring. Given the "wonderful" person I have been however, I recognize that as a tall order.

After looking at the similarities and differences in personality make-up for myself and my father, in contrast to my wife and my mother, I began to think that heart patients had two very distinct and opposite characteristics; a sensitive, warm, loving side and a selfish, cold and angry side. The more I thought about it, the more there were distinct times that I could identify when one side or the other would show up. My father, for example, was at his best when he was in control. As a doctor seeing patients in his office, my father was "The Man". He could allow the sweet, sensitive, empathic aspects of his personality to shine through. My father seemed to be happiest when he was cruising down the boulevard in his brand new Cadillac, which for him was the symbol that he had made it. (I, on the other hand prefer a Mercedes).

But a whole new dimension of my father would appear if he felt crossed or slighted in some way. Turn a report in late, and he would bite your head off. Forget to have Swiss cheese in the refrigerator, and you would think that an act of war had been declared. (For me, the absence of pretzels would be the spark that could ignite the powder keg).

In Chapter 9, I describe the narrative or "story" that we make up in an effort to make some sense of our lives. This account of our personal history has been well rehearsed, in that it has been restated many times to any one that cares to listen. The story appears very real to us, but is actually based on misinterpretations, false memories and fantasy. I discuss how certain roles are created from our stories which can be contradictory as well as limiting. For example, you will learn how I derived a "King Larry" and a "Poor Larry" role from my own story, which on the surface seemed puzzling to myself and others. When I dug deeper into the King Larry and Poor Larry roles, I discovered several interesting things. First, King Larry seemed to take charge and be in control, whereas Poor Larry seemed helpless and to have little control. Second, I discovered that King Larry seemed tough, while Poor Larry seemed vulnerable. I saw that the King role was used to hide my sensitive nature. I was *"Secretly Sensitive"*, without knowing it.

PERSONALITY CHARACTERISTICS AND HEART DISEASE

To find out more about the personality characteristics of heart patients, I reviewed the research literature. I found that the presence of depression was a risk factor for heart disease, as was hostility. Also, pessimistic, cynical and hopeless people seemed to be at risk, as were isolated people, alone without supports. To some degree, most of these traits could be used to describe my father or me. Furthermore, the research pointed to depression occurring earlier in time than heart disease, perhaps in people who were in their 20's. And evidence was found that even at the age of three, researchers could predict which children would develop depression in their 20's. These findings suggested to me that depression in childhood could lead to heart disease.

Further review of the literature revealed several attempts to classify the personalities of patients who develop heart disease.

The Type-A personality, The Hypertensive personality, and the Disease prone personality are examples of these attempts. Based on my own experience as a heart patient, observations of other heart patients including my father, and a review of the literature, I believe that there is such an entity as a "Secretly-Sensitive Personality" which I define below. Summaries of relevant studies are also presented below.

Dr. William Eaton studied 1,551 people who were free of heart disease in 1981. He found that those who were depressed were four times as likely to have a heart attack in the next 14 years. Depression in his study carried as grave a risk of heart disease as elevated levels of blood cholesterol.

A growing body of evidence suggests that a high level of depression can dramatically increase the chances of a heart attack. In a study of 730 men in Denmark, those with a high measure of depression had a 70 percent increased risk of heart attack ten years later.

People who expressed high levels of despair had a 20 percent increase in atherosclerosis over 4 years, according to research done by Susan Everson at the Public Health Institute in Berkeley, California. She found that the sense of giving up or hopelessness has the same magnitude of increased risk that one sees in a pack a day smoker. The 20 percent increase in artery narrowing persisted even in the absence of traditional risk factors such as smoking, drinking and high cholesterol.

Dr. Robert Carney found that people who have heart disease and depression are at more risk of death than non-depressed individuals with heart disease. Dr. Carney believes that depression precedes heart disease, with onset in the mid 20's, while the onset for heart disease is in the 40's and 50's for men and the 60's for women.

There is indirect evidence to suggest that the onset of depression is earlier than what is reported above. In a study by A. Caspi and T. Moffitt, it was found that behavioral differences in children as young as three years old are linked to specific adult psychiatric disorders. For example, inhibited three-year-olds were more likely at 21 years to meet diagnostic criteria for depression, than those who were not inhibited.

In a study of doctors and lawyers, Dr. John Barefoot found that doctors with high hostility were more than four times more likely to develop heart disease than doctors with low hostility. One-fifth of the lawyers in the study who had high hostility scores at age 25, were dead by age 50, while only four percent of the low-hostility lawyers died over the same period. Individuals with cynical mistrust of other people, and the frequent experience of anger were particularly vulnerable.

Research by two cardiologists, Dr. Meyer Friedman and Dr. Ray Rosenman, has been widely quoted as demonstrating a link between Type-A personality variables and heart disease. Individuals who were found to be in a constant hurry, who were intensely competitive, and had "free-floating hostility", were twice as likely to develop heart disease as the non-Type-A personalities. This proved to be the case even in the absence of other known risk factors such as smoking, drinking and overeating. Later researchers implicated free-floating hostility as the greatest single factor in the development of heart disease.

Before hypertension was treated so successfully with medications, early psychiatrists attempted to treat the condition with psychotherapy. Insights into the so-called "hypertensive personality " were gleaned from contact with the patient over extended periods of time. Dr. Franz Alexander, studied the personality of hypertensive individuals for two decades. He concluded that hypertension often resulted from unconscious conflicts that place a person in a state of hyper-vigilance or a chronic condition of fight or flight. He felt that hypertension may have its roots in the psychological conflicts of early childhood where the child was unable to have his infantile needs taken care of and understood. The child often grows up seeking support and affection, and experiences conflict whenever his anger would threaten to undermine his dependency relationships. Hostility, therefore needed to controlled; the patient would attempt to appear outwardly friendly, in order to be liked by others.

A cross sectional study conducted at the University of Hawaii provided evidence for the validity of Friedman and Booth-Kewley's notion of a "disease-prone personality". Depression, anxiety and hostility were key components of this entity. It was felt that prolonged unhappiness, in whatever form it takes, is at the root of the connection between personality and disease. Longitudinal studies which assess the relationship between heart disease and chronic negative feelings, maladaptive belief systems, inadequate social support, or poor coping skills are sorely needed according to the authors.

Scheier and Bridges identified three attributes which they feel are risk factors for physical disease: hostility, which may be characterized by a vigilant stance towards possible interpersonal stressors, such as perceived deception, coercion and manipulativeness; emotional suppression and repression, which may involve efforts to inhibit the experience and/or display of negative feelings; and disengagement, which can reflect a feeling of helplessness.

THE SECRETLY-SENSITIVE PERSONALITY: A PUSSYCAT IN TIGER'S STRIPES

Before my journey into self-understanding, I would not give much thought to the different sides of my father or myself. But now I see that the sensitive sides of my personality would only show up under conditions which were "safe", that is, where 1) there were no real or imaginary threats to my self-esteem present and 2) there was a sense of control. In the absence of these conditions, my sensitive side was nowhere to be found. It was hidden, a secret to be revealed only when conditions improved. In unsafe conditions, the pussycat part of me would run for cover.

The flip side of this phenomena, I observed, was that in conditions of threat to self-esteem or control, any of a wide variety of negative behaviors could show up, such as hostility, sarcasm, impatience and efforts to dominate. In other words while the pussycat was hiding, a ferocious tiger appeared in its place. It seemed to me that the role of the tiger was to defend the pussycat. That is, to keep potential predators from discovering the vulnerable, soft and sensitive side of the personality for fear of being hurt.

These discoveries led me to think of myself, and other heart patients, as having a *Secretly-Sensitive Personality*. I had to keep my sensitive side a secret from others so that I couldn't be hurt. The best way to keep this side a secret was to scare people away with my tough, thick-skinned, aggressive ways. All this occurred, obviously, outside my awareness. In other words, I didn't go through a conscious decision like, "O.K. Tiger, sic' em!" It simply occurred.

Over time, I had practiced this strategy so often, and so successfully, that I lost touch with the tender, loving and vulnerable aspects of myself. These valuable characteristics became a well-guarded secret, even to myself. The cost of rigidly guarding against the experience and expression of the sensitive sides of myself, in my opinion, was heart disease.

It is my belief that Secretly-Sensitive people are born with hearts that are highly reactive to stress, and overly-sensitive to perceived bad treatment such as pressure to perform, manipulation or rejection. They become hostile in response to their perceptions that others have treated them badly or will do so in the future. They shut off access to their sensitive heart when all else fails, in order to protect against painful experiences. In other words, they hide their hurt feelings, even from themselves. There is research that supports these contentions.

Evidence suggests that heart patients may have feelings that they are not aware of. For example, Richard Contrada found that certain people show increases in their heart rate without knowing it, and this pattern has been associated with physical disorders.

Several investigators suggest that heart patients will not or cannot accurately report their emotional states. It is suggested that this phenomenon may lead to undiagnosed cardiac events such as silent heart attack or prolonged treatment-seeking delay. Denial of depression was found to be positively related to coronary artery disease by Ketterer.

I am certainly not a research scientist, and my conclusions rest only upon observation and the implications of other's research findings. However, it seems to me that the Secretly-Sensitive Personality, has its roots in early childhood experiences, where some children with highly-sensitive natures are confronted with more than a fair share of rejection. Their parents, because of their own problems, are unable to give the kind of unconditional loving attention to their child that is needed. It is my opinion that the child suffers affronts to his heart on a repeated basis to the point that he learns to block out the pain by submerging his feelings. This sets the stage for depression that goes unrecognized by himself or others, anger that also had to be suppressed to protect whatever nurturance was available, and anxiety about the possible loss of needed supports. The warm, tender and sensitive side of the child originally hidden from others, eventually becomes a secret even to himself.

If my observations are correct, it seems to me that the secretly-sensitive person develops distortions in his self-image, thinking patterns, belief system, behavior and feeling states, which are then hidden from his own view. By distortions, I mean that the heart patient is not really the way he may take himself to be. He is much more than the personality he ascribes to himself, much more than his thinking patterns, belief system, behaviors and feelings, as will be seen in Chapters 10 and 11. The heart patient is unable to see his own distortions because so much of his personality is kept secret from himself. Large parts of his personality are therefore unavailable for him, which makes it impossible for him to view himself objectively. He has a tiger by the tail, and cannot see the pussycat underneath.

But in order to discover the essential features of who you really are, you need to first catch a glimpse of who you may have erroneously taken yourself to be. You are like an angel who dressed up in ragged clothes, to protect yourself from those who might take advantage of your sweet nature. The problem is that if the angel wears the ragged clothes long enough, he may actually forget he is an angel, and think that he is really a bum. He may start to think like a bum, behave in a bumly fashion, and after awhile feel all bummed out (sorry). The areas of distortion present in the secretly-sensitive heart patient include:

- *Self-image*: As a result of being raised in an environment where love and attention is based upon performance, rather than given unconditionally, the child develops low self esteem. Deep down, he perceives himself as lacking control.
- *Thinking patterns*: The child makes such errors in thinking as overgeneralization, all-or-none thinking, disqualifying positives and "should" statements.
- *Belief System*: The child comes to believe that his worth is dependent solely upon accomplishment. He develops a core belief of inadequacy or defectiveness.
- *Behavior*: Achievement, performance and productivity are emphasized in order to defend against feelings of inadequacy. Avoidance of activities that would activate feelings of inadequacy is present. Behaviors that mask emotions and perceived vulnerabilities are present as well.
- *Feelings*: The child experiences elevated levels of depression, anger and anxiety as a result of the scarcity of nurturant supplies in his environment, threats to his self-esteem and perceived lack of control.

Like peeling away an onion skin, the heart patient must learn to look deeper than he ever did before at his own personality structure. He must get in touch with aspects of himself that have heretofore been hidden. At the deepest core of his being, the heart patient is a sensitive and loving soul—an angel. This gets covered over by the personality structure in the quest for protection, as a naked man might put on ragged clothing to protect against the storm, or the pussycat may put on stripes to scare away predators. Fortunately, the personality of the heart patient can be altered and even transformed. I have learned to recognize the kinds of distortions in my life that have been outlined above, and this has provided an opening to shift how I am being at any given moment.

RECOVERING YOUR SENSITIVE NATURE

As a result of my journey into understanding, I now go through a kind of mental check list, similar to what a pilot of a plane might do before takeoff, whenever I find myself being angry or talking tough to myself. I observe what I am feeling and the way that I am behaving at the moment, what I might have been thinking prior to the feelings or behavior, and how my thoughts might relate to deep-seated beliefs about the situation or myself. I have learned that I can alter my thoughts, which brings about a change in my feelings and my behaviors.

For example, I might be caught in a long line at the supermarket. I will notice that I am starting to get angry at the slow people in front of me. I notice that I am talking under my breath, and fidgeting in place. I talk to myself, tell myself that there is no real hurry, that the world is not on hold waiting for me to emerge from the supermarket. I remind myself that the wait may be an opportunity to practice relaxation, or to go over in my mind the details of the book I am writing, or a weekend trip that is coming up. I might strike up a conversation with the person behind me in line. Generally, I feel good about myself for handling the situation in a positive way. There are other things that you, too, can do to open yourself to your softer side. We will be focusing on this goal throughout the rest of the book.

For example, forgiving others for real or imaginary hurts can help you. Try to see things from the point of view of the person you resent. Remember that the resentment is hurting you more than the other person. Try to imagine good things happening to that person.

Sharing your feelings with others in a safe place, for example a support group, can help to break down the barriers that may keep you from experiencing intimacy with others.

Volunteering your time, sharing yourself with less-fortunate people can also help you to soften your heart.

Practicing defenselessness, remembering that others are threatened by your attempts to defend yourself, may allow you to get closer to others and see aspects of them that were previously hidden.

In the next chapter you will learn to identify some of the automatic thoughts that keep a fence around your heart, such as "I'm right, you're wrong", or "You should change." By identifying your thoughts and the feelings which follow, you will take steps towards softening your heart. You will also discover a way to truly listen to others without preconceived notions of what they really mean. This will open your heart to real communication.

Later you will see that the core belief of the heart patient is defended against by behaviors which harden the heart to additional pain. By exposing this core belief as being based upon inaccurate information, the way is cleared for authenticity and openness to new experiences.

The next few chapters outline in more detail the thinking styles, belief system and defensive structure of the Secretly-Sensitive heart patient. Then the effects of negative emotions, such as anger and depression will be visited again in more detail. In the last two chapters, you will learn that the essence of who you are has nothing to do with your personality. You will see that your personality was built upon the false premise that you are inadequate or unlovable in some way. Your self-image, thinking patterns, belief system, behaviors, and feeling states have been organized around this misidentification of yourself. Once you get in touch with your essential self, you will no longer be run by efforts to hide your sensitivities. There will be no need to defend yourself against feelings of inadequacy because you will recognize the origins of your belief in childhood, where you were unable to objectively judge yourself or your situation. Furthermore, you will begin to glimpse the power within you to create your life in new ways, rather than be conditioned by past beliefs and experiences. Your personality will be less important, as you experience more joy, aliveness, and well-being in your day-to-day life. You will be more into simply Being who you naturally are, rather than behaving in ways consistent with your culturally-conditioned personality.

CHAPTER 5

WARNING: THINKING CAN BE HAZARDOUS TO YOUR HEALTH

"The heart is forever making the head its fool."
De Rochefoucauld

I know that this chapter title is a bit much, but I thought it might grab your attention. Besides, despite all the warnings from your mother to think before you act, it really is possible that the thoughts you come up with, are better left unthought. Why do I have a chapter on thoughts anyway? Everyone knows how to think. You might as well have a chapter on breathing, you might remark. (Not a bad idea, by the way). Thinking is one of those things that you take for granted, like breathing. But when you look into either one of these automatic processes, there is a lot to discover.

What I discovered from my journey into thinking, was that I was loaded down with thoughts that I wasn't even aware of. Worse, these thoughts had a major effect on my health and well-being. Worse still, was the discovery that I didn't even own many of my personal thoughts—that is they weren't even original. Lest you think that I have nothing positive to say about the results of my expedition, let me assure you that I do. Once I discovered how to find the automatic thoughts that were running me, I had a lot more control over my behaviors and my feelings. And once I was able to see the kinds of thinking errors I was making, I began to get along better with others, and I started to feel better physically. Best of all, I began to figure out which of my thoughts were similar to those of other heart patients, or belonged to a particular role I was playing, and which thoughts came from my own heart or soul.

Please join me as I continue my journey through relatively uncharted territory called "the land of unexamined thoughts". Remember why you signed up for the trip. You too have heart disease and you suspect that you might have something to do with that fact.

What could I have been thinking? Just six weeks removed from quadruple by-pass surgery and I was downing my fourth bowl of cereal before bedtime. I know I wasn't hungry because I had a big dinner, followed by several snacks while watching television.

I asked myself what it would take to finally change my bad habits if by-pass surgery had not put a big enough scare into me. I realized that I had to once and for all get in touch with the thoughts that were triggering my irrational and self-abusive behavior.

I tried to recall the events of the day with the hope that I would find the key to my overeating. I recognized that I was still mad at my wife for not being there for me in the way that I had wished. She was busy with her work, and seemed more preoccupied than usual. I told myself that she cared more for her work than she did me, and consequently I was feeling neglected, unappreciated and sorry for myself.

I tried to tie the current feelings to things that may have happened in the past, and in fact remembered that I often had felt the same way when I was left in the house as a child. My mother had to work to support the family, and I was often put in charge of my sister who was five years younger. As a child, I resented having my sister in the first place, let alone having to care for her. I wanted to be the one cared for, not the caretaker. At such times as a child, I would often raid the refrigerator, and take comfort in food. After all, food was almost always there for me, never left me once it was discovered, nearly always satisfied me, was under my control, and helped to zone me out when I was anxious or worried. When my parents tried to limit what I ate, I would sneak downstairs at night and eat whatever forbidden food I could find.

Could it be that my current situation, as an adult, was actually being reacted to as if I were still a child? Eating was a way for me to stuff my feelings of being afraid, lonely and neglected. It was a way for me to "take charge", and not feel so helpless in the face of overwhelming conditions. I was not able to appreciate the consequences of my behavior at the time of my transgression. The future really didn't seem to matter. All that mattered was the present need for immediate gratification. It was as if I had no faith that the environment would take care of me. My life seemed to be compressed into the present moment and all that really mattered was instant relief.

What kind of background could fuel thoughts and behaviors like this? For a person to be so panicked that there will not be enough for him to feel comforted and satisfied, there had to have been an absence of predictability in his background. He would have had his hopes dashed time and time again. He would have learned that he couldn't trust or rely on anyone to meet his needs, and yet sense that he couldn't meet his needs for security and love by himself. Only food could offer him fulfillment. So as an adult, he is willing to recognize that his behavior is self-defeating, but unwilling to modify or sacrifice to the degree that is necessary for his own well-being.

I refuse to gorge myself with highly -fattening foods, thus preserving a degree of virtue when I gorge myself with non-fattening foods. The problem is of course, that eating too many non fattening foods means that I gain weight because of high calorie intake. Also I have done nothing to correct the underlying problem of gorging myself in the first place. I tell myself that I deserve the extra food because of all the misfortune I have to deal with. No one can meet my needs, therefore I am entitled to what few pleasures I can take in by myself. I completely miss or ignore the fact that my present actions will hurt me in the future because the future seems so far off. Besides I will deal with the future in the future, I reason to myself.

There is a delicious quality to gorging myself anyway. I feel as though I am getting away with something. Half the fun is to sneak food so that no one will notice. What kind of background fuels the thought that I am getting away with something by stuffing myself? We were poor while I was growing up, and occasionally did not have enough to eat. I like to tell the story of having one can of Campbell's soup to feed the four of us. I also remember my father getting mad at me for ordering an extra pat of butter at a restaurant, because it cost extra. We rarely had meat at home because it was too expensive. So I am sure that I felt deprived and that there was a scarcity of food. In fact I remember that my father ate very quickly, and that unless I was pretty fast myself, I would miss out, and not get a fair share. Thus food was a highly charged issue for me as it is for most heart patients.

Participants in my heart disease support group were mostly overweight; some were even obese. They became quite fond of the dietitian, and quite knowledgeable about the fat content of foods. They modified their diets to include all the right foods, but continued to eat far more of the right foods than they should. Most did not want to deal with the underlying reasons why they stubbornly refused to limit their intake, It was if they rationalized that they were doing enough by learning what was correct. Doing the correct thing was another matter all together. Thus, who the heart patient was being did not change, and consequently what the heart patient was doing could not change for long. I think that the heart patient does just enough to appear that he is complying, while secretly harboring a belief that since no one can understand or nurture him, he will do as he sees fit. "Let's see what I can get away with", seems to be an underlying thought of a number of heart patients.

It is obvious that the heart patient must get in touch with the automatic thoughts that may be running him, in order to have any chance of changing them. But once they are identified, the heart patient needs to attack his own stubborn adherence to his belief that there is no one or anything out there that can meet his needs. He must learn what he does that reinforces his belief that no one really cares and thus justifies his self-abusive behaviors. After all, if you continually send out messages that no one can satisfy you, the world will see to it that you are correct. For example, if you are critical of your spouse's efforts to please you, you make it less likely that she will want to do that again.

In the previous chapter I talked about stress and how it affects the body. You saw that stress is an everyday fact of life. The environment, social demands, and physiological changes are all sources of stress. It is your pattern of thinking, however, which is perhaps your greatest source of stress. Cognitive therapists have demonstrated that how you think has a great deal to do with your subsequent feelings and behaviors. How a situation is appraised often determines the degree of stress you experience. If the situation is perceived as dangerous, difficult, or painful, or if your resources are perceived to be less than the situation calls for, you will experience stress. You saw how stress affects the heart in harmful ways.

In this chapter I will delve into the nature of thinking. You will see that I consider thinking to be a network of conversations you have with yourself, which is always in the background, whether you are aware of your thoughts or they occur automatically without consciousness. I will address some of the thinking patterns you and I share with other heart patients and introduce the notion that while your thoughts seem highly personal, they are in effect somewhat mechanical and predictable due to common background experiences. You will learn ways to recognize and deal with some of your automatic and erroneous thinking patterns to minimize their negative effects upon you. Thoughts that lead to more healthy behaviors and lifestyles will be presented. I will discuss the tendency of thought to expand and take over the direction of your life. I will then introduce a method for changing your thoughts. Finally, I will set the stage for the next chapter about the organization of thoughts into beliefs, which can create self-imposed limits as well as new possibilities in living.

It is hard to introduce you to information that I found to be important, without making this book seem like a college textbook. I ask you to bear with me as we go farther along. Parts of the journey through the land of unexamined thoughts, and through the land of unexamined beliefs (next chapter), may seem to have about as much excitement and adventure as listening to a lecture. But sad to say, sometimes there are no shortcuts.

THOUGHTS ARE ALWAYS IN THE BACKGROUND

Sometimes the pace of our lives keeps us so busy that we don't have time to smell the roses, let alone observe our thoughts. But if you will take a minute or two to do the exercise below, you will see that it is hard not to think, even when you are asked.

Exercise: Sit comfortably in a chair. After reading the following instructions, put the book aside. Be sure that you are near a clock or have a watch with a second hand available to you. Notice the time and close your eyes. Be perfectly still and try to clear your mind and think of nothing at all. By sense or instinct try to guess approximately when one minute has elapsed. Now put the book down and try the exercise.

What did you experience? Did you notice that thoughts kept floating in and out during the experiment, despite your efforts to clear your mind? Did you guess early on the minute or feel that the time was dragging, and that a minute in time was exceedingly long? Did you notice that you had an attitude or judgment about the exercise?

If you responded affirmatively to some of these questions, you would be similar to those heart patients who are known to be impatient, who have difficulty relaxing, and tend to be critical. This exercise demonstrates that your thoughts are an ongoing stream, ever present and always operable in the background, like a computer that can't shut off.

As I mentioned above, thoughts are so much a part of our everyday lives that we usually don't take time to "think" about them. Thoughts are for human beings like water is to fish, or air is to birds—so much a part of us that we don't take time to consider them. But I have discovered that thinking can be harmful if we're unaware of the nature and origins of our thoughts. There is much more to thinking than lies at the surface. In the next section, I'm going to dig deeper into our thought processes, get below the surface to discover where our thoughts come from and what they may saying about ourselves. I believe that thoughts which do not come from our essential selves can be dangerous and even destructive. Take a few minutes to follow me as we look more closely at the nature of thoughts.

THOUGHTS ARE CONVERSATIONS WE HAVE WITH OURSELVES

Exercise: Simply observe your thoughts for a minute and write them down. You may close your eyes if it helps you to focus upon your thoughts.

What were some of your thoughts? Typical thoughts might be "I wonder if it will rain?", or " My wife will be home in twenty minutes", or "I have to get the car fixed on Tuesday". Notice that these thoughts and perhaps your own, have a conversational quality about them, as if you were speaking to someone. Thinking then, can be thought of as a network of conversations we have with ourselves, involving speaking and listening. This becomes important later on when we discuss the importance of the listening component . We will see how our listening acts as a filter that screens and limits the information we attend to, and consequently the possibilities open to us. For example, you may listen "for" certain messages ("He's really saying I'm stupid"), rather than "to" the messenger.

TYPICAL THOUGHT PATTERNS OF HEART PATIENTS

Heart patients are similar in many ways. It is as if they joined a club without knowing it, a club composed of members who think very much like each other. Ask yourself the following questions, to see if you may be a member of the club. This is by no means meant to be an exhaustive list, just some examples of the kinds of thinking that I and other heart patients might engage in. I am reminded of Woody Allen's line that he would never join a club that would have himself as a member. Perhaps this a club that you might want to resign from, once you learn how to modify your thoughts.

- When you talk to others do you find yourself at the same time thinking of other things, or thinking critical thoughts about the person?
- Do you let seemingly little things mean a lot, spending time rehashing events over and over again?
- Do you find yourself thinking about how everything seems to happen to you?
- Do you feel unappreciated for all you have done, as if you might as well stop doing so much for others for all the recognition you are getting?
- Do you feel rushed, as though there is not enough time during the day?
- Do you think fast and find yourself frustrated by the slow, plodding thought of others?

If you recognize yourself thinking in these ways, then perhaps you are a secret member of the heart club. By recognizing these kinds of thoughts as your own, you have taken a step towards freeing yourself from their negative consequences. This is desirable because the above thoughts can be dangerous to your health. If left unchecked, these thought patterns could lead to isolation from

others, a feeling of being victimized, depression, an inability to
focus on the present, cynicism, agitation and pressure—all risk
factors for heart disease.

ARE YOUR THOUGHTS YOUR OWN?

This is another attention-getting paragraph heading designed
to keep you awake and provoke your thinking. On the surface, the
chapter heading seems silly since everyone knows that our
thoughts are our own. Who else would be thinking them? Most of
us are accustomed to the idea that our thoughts are private and
highly personal. In fact, we often retreat into our thoughts during
difficult times, regarding our minds as a refuge or safe haven.

Once you recognize, however, that your thoughts may be
similar to those of other heart patients as described above, you
may discover that your thoughts are not necessarily a personal,
individual phenomenon, but rather a somewhat mechanical
occurrence shaped by common cultural experiences. That is, you
may have a similar background to other heart patients which
creates a predictable pattern of thinking which is so automatic as
to be almost mechanical in nature. In a later chapter we will discuss
how this pattern of thoughts gives rise to a predictable future. For
example, if you constantly expect the worst, you may behave in
ways which reinforce the likelihood that you will receive what you
expect. If you believe that you are being unappreciated most of the
time, for example, you may walk around with a chip on your
shoulder, or a sour face, behaviors which are usually not
appreciated.

WHAT YOU THINK ABOUT EXPANDS

What you pay attention to or value tends to occupy more and
more of your time and attention. For example, if you are
concerned about your finances, you will spend more and more time
thinking about your bills, investments, and expenses, and less and
less time thinking about other things. If you are concerned about
crime, you may become more and more aware of media reports
about crime, may seek out protective devices, install alarms, learn
ways of defending yourself, join groups that support your
viewpoints, and generally preoccupy yourself with the issue.

In the first example, excessive worry about your finances may lead you to behave in ways which could create even more worry. For example, you may become penny wise and pound foolish, cutting corners which create additional expenses later. In the second example, you may become so fearful of others, that in your zeal to protect yourself, you may actually invite attack. A person who drives extremely slow because he is afraid of "all those crazy drivers", may unintentionally force others to drive in "crazy" ways to prevent an accident. Someone who thinks that the world is an abundant place, and who is optimistic about the future, may actually inspire others to treat him in ways that reflect his expectations. Thus, what you think about has a way of creating more thoughts in the same direction.

Heart patients who operate from the hard-hearted side of their "secretly-sensitive" personality think in negative ways. When they hide the tender parts of their personality for reasons of protection, the tiger comes out. Under these circumstances, heart patients may become critical, impatient, angry, disappointed, dominating and/or excessively competitive. They may find themselves in an ever widening circle of negative thoughts, until after a time there is little in life to celebrate or appreciate.

Your Thoughts Affect Your Feelings

Do you think that it is possible to have thoughts which just stay in your head and don't affect your feelings? I suppose that you could have a thought which on the surface is somewhat neutral, such as "That car is red." But closer examination of that particular thought would reveal an important fact. We usually have feelings attached to our thoughts, whether we are aware of them or not. For example, I may not like red cars because they seem too flashy to me. Or you may feel safer in a red car because red is so visible to other drivers. My six-year-old son would have all cars painted red, because they seem to go faster.

Of course we are talking about a rather neutral thought. What about a thought that is more loaded, like "Nothing I do is ever good enough". What feelings do you imagine might accompany that thought? If I had that thought, I might feel sad. Someone else might feel angry. There are heart patients who for defensive reasons, have learned to split off their feelings from their thoughts. These patients eventually lose touch with their feelings, and overvalue their thinking. The good news is that many of these people become corporate leaders. The bad news is that many also suffer in their relationships, and get sick.

Exercise: Read these words slowly. See if you can begin to feel emotions associated with these thoughts; Joy, silly, jolly, bright, cheerful, laughter, hilarious, energized, merriment, light-hearted, giggles, joking, fun, exuberant, gentle, amusement, gladness, pleasure, warmth, peace.
Now slowly read the following words; gloom, hardship, dread, fear, despair, disappointment, depression, frustration, melancholy, sorrow, torment, rejection, darkness, sadness, pain, regret, tears, anguish, trouble, misery.

Were you able to experience different emotions as you read each group of words? Thoughts can create feelings of well-being as well as feelings of hopelessness. Thus, your thoughts have a powerful effect upon your emotions.

WHAT YOU THINK HAS AN AFFECT ON YOUR BODY

It would be very difficult to have a thought that did not effect your body. This is because as we have seen above, thoughts affect our feelings, and our feelings reside in our bodies.

Exercise: Put your hands together in a prayer position. Clasp your fingers together. With your two index fingers slightly separated , point to the sky. Now think "fingers come together".

You may observe that your thought actually triggered a physiological response, as your fingers came together. This simple exercise demonstrates that our thoughts have a direct affect upon our bodies. What damaging effects do negative, self-critical, cynical, judgmental and/or hostile thoughts have? What about the thought " I am a failure, I just can't do it right"? It is well known that when the mind perceives a threat, hormones are released which affect the immune system, and negative thoughts can easily be perceived as threatening.
Positive thoughts can also affect the body. There is ample proof that people who take sugar pills, thinking that they are

powerful healing agents, have shown dramatic improvement in their symptoms. This placebo effect again demonstrates the link between mind and body.

You may be aware that people under hypnosis can demonstrate all kinds of effects on their bodies. For example, a hypnotized patient can actually produce blisters on his skin as a result of the thought (planted by suggestion) that his skin is being burned.

Finally, there have been reports of people with multiple personalities, who when assuming a particular personality, demonstrate allergies while in that personality but not in another. We can assume that the thinking patterns are different from one personality to another, and that physiological symptoms are affected by the particular thought pattern in ascendance.

YOUR THOUGHTS AFFECT YOUR BEHAVIORS

Imagine this situation. You are walking down the street at night. You hear a noise in the alley and think that a prowler or burglar is there. What is your reaction? You might feel tense or frightened, and hurry along. Perhaps you would gear yourself for a possible fight. Your reaction is dependent upon your assessment of the situation. If you think that the noise in the alley came from some other source, perhaps a cat playing in the alley for example, your reaction would be very different. You might be amused by the incident, or not even very interested in the event. Thus, the same incident can lead to very different feelings and behaviors depending on your thoughts.

Many people do not realize the large part that their thoughts play in their reactions. For example, suppose that your spouse said "There you go being late again," and your reaction was to get angry. Did your spouse cause you to become angry? It would certainly appear that way, since you were not angry before the remark. However, the ABC theory of cognition, very prevalent in psychology today, suggests that things are not as they might appear. The Activating event (A), in this case the statement about your lateness, was not responsible for the Consequence (C), your anger, as you might think. Rather it was your hidden Belief(B), or thought about the remark which led to your anger, according to the theory. For example, you may have thought that "My spouse shouldn't be critical of me after all that I have done." It was that thought that led to your angry reaction, not your spouse's remark.

Someone else could have had a different thought about the statement, which would have led to a different consequence.

For example, a person could have the thought "My spouse is really having a bad day and she is over-reacting to my being late." The consequence of this later thought might be to show caring and compassion for your spouse. Thus, while it may appear that an activating event creates consequences, your thoughts about the event are the important determinants of your reactions.

YOU MAY NOT BE AWARE OF MANY IMPORTANT THOUGHTS

It may be a blow to your pride to consider the notion that you may not be aware of all of your thoughts. But in truth, thoughts are coming in and out of your mind almost constantly. You would probably go crazy if every thought were attended to.

Some thoughts are easily accessed if you focus your attention. For example, if you attempt to listen to your thoughts for one minute, as was done in a previous exercise, you will become aware of most of them. However, we heart patients rarely take the time to listen to our internal conversations, so busy are we carrying on with our lives. Thus, many of our thoughts are not under our control, but rather arise spontaneously, without reflection, and often go by completely unnoticed. Yet these thoughts have a profound influence on us.

For example, in the last section we talked about an individual who had been criticized by his spouse. This person was only aware of his anger, not the underlying thought that triggered the anger. The thought itself was unconscious. These unconscious thoughts co-exist with a more manifest stream of thoughts, but are often brief and fleeting, and may be in the form of images as well as words. Most importantly, they are usually accepted as true without reflection or evaluation, causing adverse emotional, behavioral, or physiological reactions. The same automatic thought may occur time and time again when circumstances are similar. For example, whenever a heart patient feels criticized, he may have the fleeting but familiar thought that he is inadequate or unlovable in some way. Although this thought may sneak through his conscious monitor, it has the same potency as deliberate or conscious thoughts. That is, the thought can lead to emotional upset whether it is conscious or not.

THE ROLE OF AUTOMATIC THOUGHTS

Automatic thoughts are those which occur without effort or reflection, as if they come with the territory. They occur both inside and outside your awareness. In both cases they can frequently trigger adverse reactions. For example, a person may experience pain in his chest. The thoughts that follow show up automatically, without deliberation or reflection, as if the thoughts were attached to the circumstance, rather than generated by the person. Emotions, behaviors, and additional physiological responses follow close behind. Some examples follow.

An individual feels pain in his chest

Automatic thought	Emotion Physiology	Behavior	
I may die or face damage breath My pain means something bad.	fear	freeze	hold

Another example is the individual who discovers he can't walk as far as he used to following his heart attack

I don't have any control. spill I feel frustrated.	anger	fight	adrenaline

In this third example, an individual finds himself critiqued by his wife

I'll never be the same. I am no good to anyone	depression	withdrawal	lose sleep, appetite

A person who finds that he is not aroused sexually, or faces overwhelming bills may think:

I'll never perform sexually.   anxiety   avoidance   sweat, tremble
I'll never care for my family.

These examples point to the powerful effects of automatic thoughts.

What if the individuals in the above examples had different thoughts about the activating event? If the person who experienced pain had thought " I'm sore because I worked out this morning", he might not have triggered the cascade of reactions.

If the second individual had thought, "I was able to walk for ten minutes this morning, and only five minutes yesterday, " he might have had a different reaction. Similarly, if the spouse in the above example had thought " My wife really loves me and wants me to improve," instead of feeling critiqued, he might have avoided feeling depressed.

Finally the individual who was feeling anxious about his sexual performance or ability to pay bills might have had different reactions if he had thought "I can pay some bills today and some next week, I don't have to do everything at once". Or, in the case of a lack of arousal, the person could have said to himself "I am not a machine, tomorrow is another day."

Thus, the thoughts that are attendant on a particular situation, such as a pain in the chest, do not have to be automatic. You have control over what you think. As such, you can change your thoughts, and abort many of the negative consequences that automatic thoughts might generate.

HOW TO FIND YOUR AUTOMATIC THOUGHTS

In order to regain control of your thinking, and thus improve your health, you have to root out automatic thoughts, and replace them with reasoned-out, or heart-felt thoughts. To do this, it would help if you would ask yourself a basic question over and over again, " What was going through my mind at the moment?" A variation of the above would be "What do I guess I was thinking about?"

1. Ask this question whenever you notice that your feelings have changed. For example, you may notice that all of a sudden you are angry, whereas before you were mildly annoyed.

2. Ask this question whenever you are surprised by your reaction to some event, as for example an overreaction.
3. If you remember a situation in the past that upset you, or surprised you, try to picture the situation in as much detail as you can and then ask the question, "I wonder what was going through my mind just then?"
4. If needed or desired, try to role play the situation with a trusted individual in order to re-create in as much detail as possible the circumstances of the event. By so doing, you make it more likely that you can re-discover the thoughts that were operative at the time.

Once you have recognized the automatic thoughts that just show up without reflection, deliberation, or intuition, you are in a position to regain control. The next section shows you how to change the thoughts that could harm you.

QUESTIONING AUTOMATIC THOUGHTS

Now that you can identify thoughts that trigger adverse reactions, you may want to change these thoughts so as to create a more favorable reaction. To do so, you can ask yourself the following questions.

1. What is the evidence, pro and con? What is the evidence that supports this idea? What is the evidence against this idea? For example, where is it written that I have to be on time, every time. Even the President is late on occasion.
2. Is there an alternative explanation? "Perhaps my heart pain is the result of that piece of pizza with the pepperoni, sweet onions and anchovies that I just inhaled".
3. What is the worst that could happen? Could I live through it? What is the best that can happen? What is the most realistic outcome? "Chances are good that this plane won't crash. Even if it did, people are known to survive crashes. Probably, I'll just have to endure this turbulence for a few more minutes, and then enjoy the ride".
4. What is the effect of my believing this automatic thought? What could be the effect of my changing my thinking? If my friend was in a situation and had this thought, what would I tell him? "If I continue to believe that I am nothing without a lot

of money, I may drive myself into a state of exhaustion just trying to pursue the buck. If I start to think that I am worthwhile, even though I don't have a lot of material possessions, I may spend more time with the family having fun, and watching the kids grow up. If my friend asked for my advice, I would tell him to spend more time smelling the roses."

5. What is a more reasonable way to view this situation? "It's better for me to learn what I can do about my heart disease, then to feel victimized by it."

These questions can help you regain control over your automatic thoughts. This will leave you free to create your own thoughts. Since we have seen that your thoughts affect your feelings and your physiological functioning, why not create positive, life-affirming thoughts to replace damaging ones?

SOME COMMON THINKING ERRORS OF HEART PATIENTS

Just when you thought that you knew how to shift out of automatic thinking, I thought I would throw still one more challenge your way. Many of us heart patients have made it a religion to think in certain ways that can be harmful. Not only can our thoughts occur automatically, without awareness or deliberation, but those that are conscious, are often screwed up. By this I mean that they are often inaccurate, unrealistic, and just plain wrong. Some examples follow:

1. Should statements. You try to push yourself and improve yourself with shoulds and shouldn'ts, musts and oughts. I should do more, I ought to have known better, I must have a good reason for saying no. Most of the time these should statements came from our parents or teachers, and were drilled into us before we had a chance to debate their merits. Now they seem like facts to us, rather than what they really are; namely opinions.

2. All-or-none thinking. You see things as black or white. There is no gray or middle ground. Things are wonderful or awful and if what you do isn't perfect, it is a total failure. This ridiculous concept plays havoc with reality. None of us is perfect. We

operate in the middle most of the time, being reasonably intelligent, reasonably honest, reasonably good friends, etc.

3. Overgeneralizing. You see a single negative event as a never-ending pattern of defeat. If you have a misunderstanding with someone important to you, you think that person doesn't understand you or care about you, never has and never will, and for that matter, no one has ever understood or really cared and no one ever will, or can. You think you will always be isolated or misunderstood. How many times are you guilty of this kind of thinking? I bet I can beat you every time (said in my overgeneralizing manner).

4. Mental filter. You pick out a single negative detail, and dwell on that until everything is affected by that negative. If you make a nice dinner but overcook the vegetable, then you think only of the ruined vegetable until you see the entire dinner as a disaster. Do you listen for "evidence" of your inadequacies, or attempts to dominate you, or efforts to make you wrong? Or do you really listen to the person talking?

5. Disqualifying the positive. You don't count positive experiences and maintain a negative belief that is not really based on your everyday experience. You will not allow yourself to enjoy good feelings, for instance, because you will tell yourself that you know there must be bad feelings to follow. If someone makes the mistake of saying something nice about you, you may devalue the person who said it, or find some reason why he was mistaken.

6. Jumping to conclusions. You see things as negative, whether you have any facts or not. For example you may decide that someone is responding negatively to you without checking it out. Or you expect things to turn out badly, so you don't even bother doing something that could turn out neutral or even positive. Jumping to conclusions is not the kind of exercise your cardiologist prescribed for you. By the way, if you want some really good exercise, try laughing. This "inner jogging" gives the muscles of your face, shoulders, diaphragm, and abdomen a good workout, and sometimes even your arms and legs. A good laugh can burn up as many calories per hour as walking.

By recognizing these common thinking errors you have taken an important step towards freeing yourself from their negative effects. There are better ways to think. Some examples follow.

BETTER THINGS TO TELL YOURSELF

1. It is O.K. to want something or wish something. I don't have to justify my feelings.
2. Life is filled with shades of gray. Most things are somewhere in between.
3. There are no clear conclusions in life. Everything is in process.
4. All life is a choice. We establish our own set of obligations.
5. Things are probably never as good or bad as I tend to think they are.
6. My intellect is not superior to my feelings and my feelings are important to my health.
7. I will think in terms of now and the present.
8. I will not engage in mind reading
9. There is a two-thirds chance that things will be as good or better than I expect, and only a one third chance that things will be worse than I expect.
10. You have thousands of behaviors every day. A few of them may be negative by chance alone. That means you can be proud of hundreds of positive behaviors every day.

RE-TRAINING YOUR MIND

Since most of your thoughts are the result of your experiences in the world, they are similar to those of many other people who have had similar experiences. In order to train your mind to have thoughts that you choose to have, rather than thoughts conditioned by others and your past, you would need to reverse the typical thought- word- deed sequence. For most people, the process of creation is to first have a formative idea or concept. Next the thought is put into the form of words, either written or spoken, Finally, the words may be put into action. We are taught to think before we act from early childhood.

If you want to change your thinking rapidly, simply reverse the process by acting first. Then put your action into words for others to hear. You will eventually develop a new thought based upon repetition of your actions.

There have been many times in my life, usually when the stakes were high, that I acted before thinking, went with my gut before my mind had a chance to talk me out of my decision. Not all of these actions resulted in positive outcomes, at least on the surface. Of course, many of my reasoned-out decisions were not so hot either. Still, my greatest joys were the result of my spontaneous actions. Following your heart can lead to openings in your life that you only dreamed of.

WHAT WE HAVE LEARNED

Thoughts are mental representations which are ever present, and always operating in the background or on a moment to moment basis, like a computer that can't turn off. Thinking can be considered simply as a network of conversations you have with yourself, involving internal speaking and listening. Heart patients often think in similar fashion to one another, suggesting that your thoughts are not necessarily a personal, individual phenomena, but rather a somewhat mechanical occurrence shaped by similar backgrounds and experiences. Heart patients have thoughts about getting things done quickly, being in control, fulfilling obligations, finding fault, etc. They make common thinking errors, such as all or none thinking, overgeneralizing, disqualifying the positives and should statements. Since what is focused upon has a way of expanding, heart patients who think negatively tend to experience more and more negatively-charged events. Expecting the worst, they often unconsciously arrange for the worst to happen. Thoughts affect the body in positive ways as is demonstrated by the placebo effect, and negative ways by creating stress and tension. The same incident can lead to very different feelings and behaviors depending upon what you think about the incident.

Many thoughts operate at an unconscious or automatic level. You can learn to identify and challenge these automatic thoughts to reduce their unwanted effects. Common thinking errors can thus become conscious and be replaced with more adaptive thoughts. You can also learn to reverse the thought - word - deed sequence in order to learn the process of thinking your own, rather than conditioned thoughts.

In the next chapter we will discuss how thoughts, in the form of beliefs, influence the heart patient's health, self-image, problem-solving abilities, and possibilities for well-being.

CHAPTER 6

BELIEVING IS SEEING

*"...Be not afraid of life. Believe that life is worth living,
and your belief will help create the fact.*
William James

In the last chapter I suggested that our thoughts are conversations we have with ourselves. I stated that this network of conversations is not a personal, individual phenomena, as it seems, but rather is a mechanical occurrence shaped by culture and family. For example, people with heart disease may have very similar thoughts because of similar experiences. Furthermore these conversations are continuous and ongoing. It is difficult to turn off the "chatter" that fills your mind.

The distinction was also made between thoughts you are aware of and seemingly control, and automatic thoughts which arise spontaneously, without reflection, and often go by completely unnoticed. You are more likely to recognize the emotion associated with the automatic thought than the thought itself. For example, a person might notice that he is angry before recognizing that he had the thought, "That person just criticized me unfairly." You did exercises that illustrated how thoughts affect your physiological and emotional states. You also learned that your listening is an active, rather than a passive process, in that you tend to listen for information based upon your thoughts and beliefs.

The chapter title, *Believing is Seeing* means that how you see things is strongly influenced by your underlying beliefs. Psychologists use ink blots and other projective tests which are based on this observation. Even in what might seem to be a cut-and-dried situation, such as an eye-witness account of a crime, witnesses to the same event may report seeing things quite differently depending upon whether they were called to the stand by the prosecution or the defense.

In Chapter 8, I will talk at length about the Type-A personality and its effect on the heart. Such qualities as suspiciousness, cynicism, alienation, anger, irritation, hostility, aggravation and impatience have been associated with the Type-A personality and increased risk of heart disease. A person who constantly tries to prove himself worthy of others' love and approval by hard work, may feel hostility and cynicism if he feels unloved and unappreciated. He may not be aware however, that underlying his negative and damaging feelings is a set of beliefs involving his sense of entitlement, his hyper-sensitivity to perceived disapproval, and his exaggerated need for control.

In this chapter, you will examine some of the beliefs that you share with other heart patients. I will show how these beliefs can damage your heart, lower your self-esteem, interfere with your experiences, retard problem solving, and limit your possibilities for the future. I will discuss how these beliefs came about and how they become part and parcel of who you are. You will begin a process of unraveling your negative beliefs and your identification with them by questioning their origins in perception. In the next chapter, beliefs that are more adaptive will be distinguished from those that are less adaptive. Most important however, will be the laying of the groundwork for a kind of "master" belief. This belief focuses upon the nature of your essential self, your spirit or soul if you like, and creates the maximum opportunity for growth and well-being. It opens up new possibilities in living and reduces the negative effects of your past conditioning and experiences.

WHAT IS A BELIEF?

A belief is a group of thoughts accepted as absolutely true. A thought becomes a belief when it is reinforced by experience or repeated observation. For example, if you grow up in a home with a domineering father and a submissive mother, you may have thoughts that women are "weak-willed". When internal conversations are repeated frequently enough and over a long enough period of time, they achieve the status of a belief, accepted as true automatically and without question.

When I believe something to be true, I have a sense of conviction about it and an emotional charge on it as well. Beliefs are not dependent upon facts or scientific evidence in order to exist. In the example above, there is no scientific evidence that women are deficient in will-power. In fact the quote "Hell hath no fury like a woman scorned!", would suggest quite the opposite. As is true about thoughts, beliefs are always in the background influencing your perceptions and interpretations in a mechanical manner. That is, they crop up automatically without reflection, as if a button were pushed.

However your beliefs are much harder to bring to consciousness than thoughts. Often you have to infer what your belief may have been based upon your feelings or behaviors. For example, you may find yourself frequently ignoring a co-worker but be unaware that you have a belief about his age, race, or educational level which causes you to ignore him.

Another example occurred in my group. As was my practice, I would ask group participants to complete an evaluation form for each session. One participant wrote "Too much time is allowed for questions which do not apply to the topic. You should prevent certain clients from wasting time in areas of no concern. You should not stop midstream and ask 'What do you think? Give me some feedback. Do not allow yourself to be interrupted by a client who only wants to hear himself talk".

This person suffered from intense headaches as well as severe heart disease. While well-meaning, he was unaware of his underlying Type-A belief structure, involving competitiveness, impatience, need for control, and concern about productivity. His surface behavior appeared to be angry, abrupt and somewhat curt, hardly warm, accepting or tolerant. This example illustrates an important point about beliefs, namely that they underlie emotions as well as behaviors.

WHAT DO YOU BELIEVE?

Please answer true or false to the following statements:

| | True | False |

People should speak up when they have something to say.
You have to struggle in life.
Nothing good comes easy.
People ought to have the same values and
perceptions that I have.

Your worth is dependent upon what you produce.
It's a dog-eat-dog world, and people are not to be trusted.
Children should be seen and not heard.
Unlike others, I don't deserve to suffer life's obstacles and
inconveniences.

People should get to the point and not beat around the bush.
Life is about numbers. The more you have the better you are.
My anger is justified and caused by the ignorance and
incompetence of others.

Giving and receiving love and affection are signs of weakness.
People should be polite at all times.
I have to be in charge.
I have to make more money.
I like or need to be in control.
Because of my intellectual, economic or moral superiority, I
should never be challenged or criticized.

There's no task which I cannot perform well.
Big boys don't cry.
No matter how capable I am, I could have done better.
I must get everything done on time.
I must finish work before I play.
I get annoyed quickly when criticized.
I feel like lashing out when even little things go wrong.
I look for the opportunity to get even or to pay back
people who wrong me.
I check up on other people to see if they are doing their job
properly.

Perhaps this exercise will help you to identify one or more of your beliefs. Which ones are true for you? Are there other beliefs that you can identify? Write them down. Notice that the beliefs that you have quickly checked as true by you are without question or reservation. Notice that it doesn't typically occur to you that a different point of view may be correct. Furthermore, can you see that your endorsement of a particular belief directs how you behave? For example, if you believe that your worth is dependent upon your accomplishments, you may find yourself working very hard to produce.

Perhaps not so noticeable is the notion that your belief may actually determine what you see or hear. For example, if you believe that people should be polite, you may not listen to what someone has to say who is perceived by you as rude. Or if you believe that your spouse should get to the bottom line, you may not hear his communication if it seems to ramble. In the examples above, if you found yourself answering *true* to many, or even <u>most</u> of the questions, you would be responding in similar fashion to some of the heart patients in my practice, and patients who have been characterized as Type-A personalities. As a heart patient myself, I, too, share some of the same beliefs.

Once a belief is entrenched, it feels like a rock-solid foundation from which you live your life. For example, the belief that a particular religious group is inferior may lead an individual or group to discrimination and even war. What beliefs exist in a given culture will determine many of the behaviors of the people in that culture.

For example, when we believed that the world was flat, few people ventured far into the ocean for fear of falling off the earth. People were burned at the stake for being "witches". No one could understand why so many women and children died at childbirth But with the shift in beliefs from "It was God's will.", to germ theory, came the discovery of antibiotics. Thus beliefs can limit or extend what is possible.

In a positive way beliefs can help to protect and guide us. For example, "I shouldn't cross the street in traffic", could be a lifesaving belief. Other beliefs may have short-term gains such as financial success, but may have long-term consequences such as alienation, self absorption, or illness. An example of such a belief is "I must do more than others to be worthy." Knowing what our beliefs are is the first step towards self-control. By determining which beliefs are worth keeping and which are best questioned or disputed, we increase our chances of health and well-being.

BELIEFS ARE SEDUCTIVE

The capacity of culture to control thoughts and beliefs is awesome. Similarly, the attraction that human beings have to fit in with others and to surrender to conventionality is everywhere to be found. Whether because of insecurity or a need to belong, individuals feel pressured to become one of the herd. What is often lost is our own unique character or nature and our own unique path. By having the courage to step back and examine our beliefs, we can load the dice in favor of leading an authentic and healthy life.

HOW YOU DEVELOPED YOUR BELIEFS

Many of us with heart disease share certain similarities in our early lives which leave us vulnerable. Chief among them is early loss. Early loss is defined as the unavailability of a parent or the loss of a parent's time and/or loving affection due to the physical and/or emotional unavailability of the parent. Examples of early loss include physical absence due to death, illness or divorce of a parent, separation from the parent due to long hours at work, or the emotional unavailability of the parent due to problems the parent is facing in dealing with divorce, alcoholism or other stressful events. In my case, my father was frequently in the hospital, my mother worked full time to support the family, and my sister and I were often cared for by relatives or neighbors.

Early loss can result in a decrease of unconditional acceptance of a child (where a child is loved for just being who he or she is), and an increase in conditional love (where a child is valued only for what he or she accomplishes, or how he or she performs). I remember that my parents praised me on the rare occasions that I received a good report card in school, or behaved properly with their friends, but I don't remember getting hugs and kisses "for no good reason". The end result is that I experienced quite a bit of anger and rejection, along with doubts about my self-worth.

With experiences such as mine occurring over and over again in childhood, the future heart patient develops a core belief that he is deficient in some way (helpless, unlovable, incompetent, and/or inadequate). Strategies you can use to ward off this core dysfunctional belief will be discussed in Chapter 7.

It is important to understand that this core belief is so deeply engrained and so well-defended against that you will most likely not be aware of its existence. Rather, you will more likely consciously regard yourself as just the opposite. You will probably see yourself in favorable ways, as capable and worthwhile, and your childhood as normal, appropriate, and/or positive.

Patients in my group described themselves in the following positive ways: "I am an encourager and motivator", "I consider myself to be a problem solver", "I am fun-loving and outgoing". Several described their childhood experiences in positive terms as well: "My parents sacrificed their lives to provide a good education for me." "My parents were hard-working and I never wanted for anything." "Even though our family was poor, I cannot recall being unhappy because everyone around me was the same." Only after several sessions did these patients reveal deep-seated hurts.

Thus heart patients may tend to minimize or deny any pain caused by early home experiences. Similarly, it may also be difficult for them to see the compensatory nature of their need for perfection, accomplishment, and accumulation of symbols of success. When you come from a true deficiency-orientation your behavior is organized around attempts to get satisfied or to survive, rather than from the experience of being satisfied in the moment. Instead of a life organized around the expression of being complete and whole now, such a life becomes one of striving and struggle for some future pay off.

THE PROBLEM WITH BELIEFS

Once you form a belief, it becomes a very powerful influence. You can become righteous about your beliefs and resentful when others don't see things your way. You may also become regretful when you don't do something that you think you "should have" done. Once you become aware of how beliefs develop however, and of their somewhat arbitrary nature, there may be less of a desire to add additional beliefs to your baggage without a good deal of deliberation. You become less of a "true believer" and more open to other points of view.

Beliefs are suspect for the following reasons: they may be inaccurate; they may limit experience; they can pre-determine your future; and they may limit your potential.

BELIEFS MAY BE INACCURATE

Our beliefs rest on perceptions which may be unreliable. When we look at the sun moving across the sky, the earth seems to stand still. We experience ourselves as still in a car or train. Yet in both examples we are moving. The human eye perceives only a narrow band of stimulation, less than one-billionth of the stimuli in a room. How much do we miss when we judge another person? Can we put ourselves in another's shoes when trying to resolve conflicts?

Our perceptual apparatus responds to major changes, but not to gradual changes. In an earlier chapter, we talked about the unfortunate frog that was gradually exposed to increasingly-heated water. Unfortunately, the frog did not sense the gradual build-up of heat and therefore could not jump out of the boiling water to save his life.

It seems that we human beings have a similar problem recognizing gradual changes that put us in hot water. Like the frog's, our nervous system is geared to react to rapid and dramatic changes, and to accommodate or habituate to gradual trends. This tendency has value when we must react to immediate threats, like a heart attack or a flash of lightning, but it does not help us in circumstances which are potentially deadly, but more gradual, such as the slow build-up of plaque in our arteries, or to circumstances to which we have adapted or accommodated erroneously.

We seem to be programmed or wired to register short-term, moment-to-moment changes while we ignore the background or backdrop. We look for discrepancies and ignore what is going on constantly. We respond to sudden shifts, while perception of gradual long-term changes has been suppressed in our evolution. We recognize when an air conditioner comes on or goes off, but we soon forget or ignore its constant hum. We adapt to toxic circumstances in our families without realizing the damage done to us. We develop beliefs that are limiting, disabling and potentially deadly without awareness. Our nervous systems do not prepare us for the gradual poisoning of our planet or ourselves because they are geared as short-term reactive mechanisms.

In the realm of medicine, the boiled frog syndrome shows up as a focus on the dramatic cures that may be found while ignoring the more prevalent issues of lifestyle problems and the effects of beliefs on illness. What prevents us from perceiving damaging trends is our need to see things as constant or unchanging. Our nervous system evolved over millennia to regard the status quo as safety. No news is good news for the nervous system. We pay attention to beginnings and endings of things and ignore the middle. Our beliefs are ways of simplifying or ignoring information in order to preserve our notion of safety.

Beliefs are often inaccurate because our motivation and needs affect our perceptions. A thirsty man may see a mirage in the desert. A needy and desperate person may misperceive a con artist as someone who can help him. A person who believes that others are out to humiliate him may perceive criticism or sarcasm where none was intended.

Another reason that beliefs are inaccurate is that we influence what appears to be reality. Two mythical situations will serve as examples.

THE FARFEL BIRD EXPERIMENT

A scientist wants to study the mysterious Farfel bird in its natural habitat. The scientist digs a hole in the ground from which to observe Farfels up close. Whenever he pops his head out of the ground, he observes Farfels running around in a state of frenzy and holding their long noses. He concludes that Farfels are very nervous birds with strange habits. Later, NASA decides to study Farfel birds via satellite observation and finds them to be relaxed and productive. Although one famous scientist says that the Farfel bird is a nervous bird, the spokesperson at NASA states that the Farfel bird appears that way possibly because it has a particular aversion to the smell of human beings. People believe that things are a certain way without realizing that they may appear that way because of their influence.

THE TRAVELING SALESMAN STORY

A traveling salesman runs out of gas. He sees a remote farmhouse and takes his gas can to ask the farmer for help. He has doubts about his reception by the farmer because it is late at night. He vacillates and feels the farmer will be mad at him or mistake him for an intruder. He's about to knock on the door, when he decides that the farmer is going to get mad and that he should have waited until morning. Just then the farmer opens the door. Having worked himself into a lather, the salesman hits the farmer over the head with his gas can saying "I knew you wouldn't give me any gas you S.O.B!", and he storms off in a huff. The farmer grabs his shotgun and peppers the salesman with pellets. The salesman runs away and berates himself for going to the farmer's house against his better judgment. In other words, he got exactly what he expected.

Thus it is difficult to sort out how much of a particular belief is a result of your accurate observations, or a product of your own contaminating interventions. Such is the nature of a "self-fulfilling prophecy" where expectations can determine the outcome of a situation.

Other people may judge and evaluate us, and yet their perceptions and beliefs are biased, like ours. It is difficult for a young child to have the perspective and presence of mind to be able to understand that a hurtful comment from an emotionally-upset parent may be less an accurate portrayal of that child, and more a reflection of the parent's emotional state.

In summary, beliefs can be inaccurate because they are based on a perceptual apparatus which is often limited in accuracy, is relatively non-reactive to gradual but harmful events, is affected by our motivation and needs, is influenced by our actions, and is often based upon others' biased perceptions.

BELIEFS LIMIT EXPERIENCE

Read this sentence aloud.

Can you experience something and have a thought about it at the the same time?

Now read the same sentence aloud again. Did you notice that you may have missed an extra word in the sentence. If you did not discover the extra word right away, try to remember your thoughts at the time. Were they critical of the writer or publisher for "mistakenly" including the exercise in the book? Did you feel tricked? Were you being self-critical for not finding the missing word? What you said to yourself is an important clue to what you believe. Thus, while you were busy thinking about the exercise process or about the content of the exercise, you may have missed the experience of an accurate reading. It is difficult to be in an experience and in your mind at the same time.

Having a belief that this exercise is boring, for example, will be different from the actual physiological experience of boredom which may involve sleepiness or yawning. Most of us are out of touch with our bodily sensations, particularly heart patients who are too often conceptual and analytical.

Here is another exercise. Try to connect the circles using four straight lines without lifting your pencil from the paper.

o   o   o

o   o   o

o   o   o

Most people would find this very difficult and give up in frustration. What may prevent you from seeing the solution is a belief that there is an invisible barrier around the circles and that the circles are in a kind of box. The solution to the problem lies in going outside the invisible "barriers" as illustrated below.

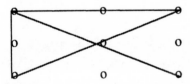

This problem can actually be solved using one straight line. But doing so requires that you give up the limited, self-imposed and self-created belief that only a certain size pencil would be acceptable. A pencil the size of a paint brush would be wide enough to cover all circles at once.

Thus some beliefs can limit your ability to solve problems. What other self-imposed limits have you created that rob you from living life fully? Perhaps, "I am too old or sick to do anyone any good." Where is that written? Go outside your self-imposed limitations by questioning your beliefs. Don't live your life in a box.

At any given moment you have a choice in life—to remain stuck in a particular limiting belief, or to allow yourself to experience the moment. If you find yourself trying to prove to others that you are right about your beliefs, you may be sacrificing a certain level of openness to other points of view.

For example, you may meet someone who is dressed more casually than fits your taste and conclude that he is beneath you in status. Believing this, you may not be open to the possibility that this person has something valuable to teach you. You may find your mind is someplace else in your interaction with him, thereby cutting yourself off from the full experience of him as a potentially rich human being. It is best to learn to pay attention to your bodily sensations and emotions without judgment or evaluation.

There is a knowledge which is not dependent upon interpretation or belief but instead is rooted in physiological responses. It is possible to recognize in the "gut" the presence of a new idea even before you know exactly what it is. You may not be accustomed to letting yourself really experience life. This is because you may be more accustomed to thinking about your experiences, remembering past events, considering future events, than to actually allowing yourself to be in the present moment. When you are busy analyzing an experience, pulling it apart and dissecting it, you have killed that experience. Even the thought "I am happy now" takes you out of the experience of being happy.

WHEN BELIEFS BECOME REALITY, THEY PRE-DETERMINE YOUR FUTURE

All of us are born in a helpless and dependent state. We come to rely upon our parents and other caregivers to protect and guide us. Over time we accept as true their admonitions and prohibitions. How many times have we heard in our youth "Don't touch that stove!", or "Stay away from strangers!"? Since our physical and emotional survival may depend upon pleasing our caregivers we eventually internalize their messages and no longer require their physical presence.

We eventually create our own internal watchdog which often speaks with the same words and intonations that our original caregivers used. These thoughts and beliefs may become automatic, so frequent and routine that they are no longer recognized by us. Like the fish who doesn't know he is swimming in water, you may become so accustomed to your internal conversations that you no longer differentiate them from reality. Your beliefs become your reality. You don't *have* beliefs, you *are* your beliefs.

In other words, a person who believes that things must be done quickly and efficiently, as is the case with many heart patients, will behave in ways consistent with this belief. He will "be" an organized, no-nonsense person, focused and directed towards task completion. He will not allow himself to be interrupted by "extraneous" matters such as his effect upon other people. Such a person believes himself to be operating in accordance with the principles of reality. He doesn't question the correctness of his position, for in his mind he is being realistic. He doesn't recognize that he has adopted a belief that directs his actions. He typically doesn't go that "deep" into his motivations. "That's just how things are", would be sufficient thought for this person. In Chapter 7, I will discuss in greater detail how people can misidentify themselves with their beliefs. I will also explore what it means to be "realistic".

This process can be further illustrated by examining how elephants are trained. The trainer will tie a heavy chain to the leg of the baby elephant and attach the chain to a large tree. The small elephant pulls and fights and finally realizes that he can't escape. Over time, the trainer uses thinner chains and smaller trees but the elephant still perceives "Chain and Tree", and doesn't pull away. Finally it is possible to have a full-grown elephant remain in place by a rope attached to a sapling. He believes he is chained and so he is.

Believing is seeing! Believing determines what's possible. Fleas in a jar will bounce off the lid trying to escape. Later when the lid is removed the fleas will remain in the jar. They have learned "their limits".

BELIEFS MAY LIMIT YOUR POTENTIAL

One of the problems we face as human beings is that we often don't know what we believe, so automatic and ingrained are our belief systems. We are better able to recognize our emotional reactions than the underlying beliefs. For example, I may easily recognize my impatience at standing in a long line, but be less aware of my belief that people should not be treated like cattle. I may recognize my anger at my boss, but be unaware that he triggered my belief that I should be perfect and always on time with my work.

Even if we recognize a particular belief that we have, we rarely question its accuracy. Our beliefs seem like facts to us, almost as if that is who we are. For example, if you lost the use of your arm in an accident, would you still be you? Most people would say that although not quite the same, they are still essentially themselves. What if you also lost your ability to walk? Would you still be you? Most people would say that although they wouldn't be exactly the same because of the required changes in their lifestyle, they would still recognize themselves.

But what if you were cut off from your beliefs, as for example, by suffering from amnesia, or by being detained as a prisoner of war in a foreign country without benefit of social supports. Would you still be you? Most people would no longer see themselves as separate from their beliefs. That is, they would identify themselves with their beliefs. For many of us *are* our beliefs. We live in a world where wars are fought on a daily basis with each side believing strongly in the rightness of its position. People will fight to the death if necessary to uphold their beliefs. Beliefs thus can take precedence over happiness or even life itself.

What beliefs are so entwined in your personality that they are not recognized as beliefs, but are instead seen as obvious facts? "I must produce in order to be valued."? "A man must take care of his family's finances."? "Laziness is a sin.."? "We have no say in what happens to us."? What beliefs do you have that are so much a part of who you are, that you are limited in what you will do or try? "I'm not good at speeches."? "I don't do hugs"? "Why bother, I'll only fail."? "People will laugh at me."?

Exercise: Make a list of some things you have always wanted to do but never did. What beliefs prevented you from doing these things? For example, "I'm too old.", or "I'm not smart enough.", might be beliefs that could prevent a person from trying something new.

Take three or four characteristics of the beliefs you identify and make a costume in your mind that would depict these characteristics. In the example above, a dunce cap and a cane could depict someone who is too old or too stupid to do a particular thing. Try to feel what it would be like to go out with such a costume. Picture yourself wearing the costume to the supermarket, for example, and try to imagine the reactions of other people to seeing such a sight. Try to get in touch with being that costume while wearing it.

Now imagine a different costume, perhaps the opposite of the one you created. For example, think of a young man in a cap and gown. Try to imagine yourself in the supermarket with this costume as well. Feel the difference between having a costume that you can put on and take off, and being that costume. Who is the actor that puts on the costume? Who is the actor that adopts particular beliefs?

You will see that you are bigger than the beliefs that you have. Take away your beliefs and there is something substantial left. It is called the "spirit", "soul", "potential", "capacity" or "empty space" by different people. What is left is a context which has no form or content or position, but instead gives rise to them. We will talk about this *essential you* in Chapter 10.

WHAT WE HAVE LEARNED

A belief is a group of thoughts accepted as absolutely true. When your internal conversations are repeated over and over again, you come to believe that they are factual. After a while many of your beliefs fade into the background and become like water to the fish, so much a part of you that you cannot distinguish yourself from your beliefs. Once established, you are programmed or conditioned to react in a mechanical way to events, with little choice in the matter. Your beliefs can help direct and guide you, but also limit what is possible for you to see.

Many of our fellow heart patients have been subject to early losses in their lives, experienced parental unavailability, anger and/or rejection. A self-concept was formed based on conditional approval. "I am not deficient as long as I produce". You may not be able to see the compensatory nature of your achievement orientation, nor would you be likely to question the underlying accuracy of your beliefs, yet beliefs are suspect because the perceptions that they rest on are often inaccurate. You respond to major but not gradual changes, your motivation and needs affect your perceptions, and you have influenced what appears in front of you. Still it is difficult to overcome the seductiveness of believing in conventional ways, so important is it for you to fit in. You *believe* often at the cost of experience, pre-judging events to the point that you are often not open to new experiences.

CHAPTER 7

DEFUSING DAMAGING BELIEFS

"It is always easier to believe than to deny.
Our minds are naturally affirmative."
John Burroughs

We have seen how stress can lead to biochemical changes such as increased heart rate, breathing rate, muscle tension, metabolism, and blood pressure. When stressors are unrelenting, as in major work changes, marital problems, or coping with chronic illness, the mind perceives a threat and the body becomes alarmed or aroused. Adrenal glands continue to secrete norepenephrine indicating that blood is to be directed to the brain and muscles, and away from organs that are nonessential to fighting or fleeing, like the liver.

However, the liver is now impeded from processing sticky LDL (bad) cholesterol which circulates in the bloodstream longer and begins to clog coronary arteries. The release of stress hormones like adrenaline, can work the heart muscle so hard that it can collapse with exhaustion. It is well known that anger and hostility trigger adrenaline which raises blood pressure, makes the blood clot more rapidly, and accelerates a host of other physiological processes that are likely to speed the growth of plaque in the arteries. It is important to emphasize that for adrenaline to be released in the first place, the mind must perceive that there is a threat. External events in themselves do not constitute a threat. For example, a job loss or separation may be threatening to one person, but seen as an opportunity or challenge to another.

Therefore it is your internal reaction to the situation that determines whether or not there is a threat.

Certain beliefs make it more likely that you will respond to a situation as a threat, and other beliefs load the dice in favor of a more adaptive response. This will be discussed below.

Beliefs That Trigger Stress

Certain beliefs make it more likely that your mind will perceive a situation as a threat. If you believe that your behavior is controlled by the environment, then you will blame the environment when things go wrong. For example, if you are caught in traffic, you could experience the situation as unfair, feel victimized, and fume with impatience and irritation. You will feel victimized, as though what happened is not fair. You might ask "Why me?" On the other hand if you believe that the environment can be changed through your own personal efforts you may try harder or tell yourself "I'll show them". You may lean on the horn, scream out verbal abuses or drive recklessly, all behaviors which reveal aggravation and anger.

What these two beliefs have in common is the idea that things should be a certain way. The drivers should be more courteous, or better prepared—the roads should have more lanes, or "I should have taken a different route". Whether the environment is seemingly to blame or the self, the underlying problem is the dictatorial, arrogant, narcissistic demand that things should be different from what they are. Heart patients in particular have a hard time accepting what is. They are quick to find fault and attempt to change or control things to fit their beliefs. Do you recognize any of these "should" beliefs?

I should have been farther ahead in my job by now.
I should never quarrel with my spouse.
I must work as hard as my father did.
He should have been more polite.
They should have known better.
I must take care of everyone who cares for me.
I must not make mistakes.
People should endure hardship with equanimity.
She should know what my needs are by now.
I must do more than others to prove I'm worthy.

I must prove myself over and over, again because past accomplishments don't count.

I must always keep striving to improve.

I should be bigger, prettier, younger, thinner, richer, nicer, better.

A key belief that seems to characterize heart patients is "My worth is dependent upon my accomplishments." This belief leads to a vicious cycle which lowers self-esteem and intensifies the behavior pattern.

Efforts to accomplish many things....

Creation of time-urgent behaviors, anger and frustration when things don't go well, fatigue...

Exhibition of tension, anger, irritability, critical, demanding, impatient...

Others feel uneasy, threatened, annoyed, put down, angry, disgusted...

Others may respond by withdrawal, dislike, confrontation, avoidance, rejection...

Feedback from others lead to thoughts of, People, don't like me or want to be around me. I'm not lovable...

Sense of deficiency, lowered self-esteem...

Compensatory thought of, "I may not be lovable, but I can get respect, admiration and maybe approval by being better and faster..."

Efforts to accomplish many things...

SOME BELIEFS CAN ACTUALLY PROTECT YOU FROM STRESS

If you believe that any human action can be explained by the interaction between personal and environmental influences, then you will be less likely to blame yourself or others. When this belief in causality is followed, you will consider the contribution of many factors such as the other person's role, the situation itself, your own behavior in the situation, your perception of the situation, and your physiological and emotional responses to the situation. For example, if you are caught in traffic, you might consider that the problem has to do with the time of day you chose to travel, and remind yourself of the positive reasons that you chose that particular time and that particular route. Your stress level will decrease as a result of this mind-set.

If you believed that the environment may not be malleable, but that you can control your own reactions, you will also reduce your stress level. You may accept that there are many environmental factors that are beyond control. Therefore efforts to exert direct change over such factors are doomed to fail.

Control over the situation requires a shift from attempting direct control of the event to control of the way you perceive the event. For example, you may be caught in traffic and realize there is nothing you can do about it. You may choose to make it okay with yourself, appreciate the extra time to practice deep breathing or listen to music or talk on the car phone or tape recorder or just quietly "be" without the need for doing anything.

Examples of Positive Beliefs:
I have choices about how I solve problems.
I cannot control anyone but myself.
I have the power to change.
It is not necessary for me to prove anything to anyone.
I can trust that things will work out without my intervention.
I can only live in this precious moment.
To err is human
I am lovable.
Everyone exists with a need to be loved, not judged.
I am growing as a person and that is what is important.
My safety and strength lie in being less defensive.

CHANGING YOUR USE OF CERTAIN WORDS CAN HELP YOU SHIFT BELIEFS

Words and language are to beliefs what shapes and colors of beliefs are to a painter's canvas. Choosing your words carefully can create vastly different outcomes. Remove yourself from the tyranny of the "shoulds". Most heart patients preface their beliefs with the word "should", as in "I should be more successful". Equivalents of the word "should" are "must" (as in "I must work long hours in order to be successful"), "ought to" (as in "People ought to be polite"), and "have to" (as in "I have to struggle in order to survive").

Try to notice how often you use "shouldisms". Enlist the aid of a loved one to "catch you" in your use of these automatic words. Ask him or her to help you rephrase your sentence using the words "I want to" or "I wish to", "I prefer to", or "I would like to". For example, if you are "caught" saying, "You should return the car with gas when you borrow it.", try to rephrase the sentence by saying "I would prefer it if you would fill the car with gas once you have used it". You may feel that this is a very minor point, but psychologists can tell you that their practices are filled with people who are unable to recognize how much pressure they put on themselves by "shoulding all over the place". There is more freedom in stating your wish or preference, and less defensiveness elicited in others when you merely state your wish, rather than what often appears to be a demand. People don't like being told what they should do or shouldn't do. In fact, the excessive anger and hostility of the heart patient can be related to the overuse of these words.

When you believe that things should be a certain way and they are not, you have set yourself up for anger and its damaging effects on the heart. Other terms that are similarly absolute in nature and therefore invite negative responses are, "always", "never", "all", "none", "everything" and "nothing". Substitute words like "usually", "often", "occasionally", "seldom" for the words above, and you will probably invite less argument.

Exercise - Please answer these questions.
1. What kind of person does what he wants to most of the time?
2. What kind of person does what he should most of the time?

Please take a moment to think about these questions and write down your answer. If you are like the heart patients in my group who were given these questions as a homework assignment, you would have negative reactions to the person in the first sentence, and positive reactions to the second. Examples from the group are that the person who does what he should is "a very kind and caring person," "thoughtful of himself and others", "careful and orderly". Whereas a person who does what he wants was perceived as "self-indulgent", "a very self-centered person", "assertive and selfish", or "arrogant". These remarks are interesting from the point of view that the heart patient tends often to be opinionated and judgmental in his response. This may be because in their childhood, heart patients may not have been typically allowed the "luxury" of doing what they wanted, but instead were regarded conditionally based upon doing what they were supposed to do.

It is possible to respond to the two questions above in exactly the opposite way than the group. For example, it can be reasoned that people who do what they should all the time are less imaginative, followers rather than leaders, less likely to think for themselves, and robot-like in their experiences. People who do what they want all the time can be perceived as self-directed, happy, innovative, and movers and shakers. Heart patients tend to be black and white in their thinking styles. They find it difficult to see both sides of the coin.

Although words like "I", "me", "my" are good to use when prefacing what you stand for, when there is too much focus on the self, others are turned off. You are perceived as selfish, narcissistic, self-absorbed, and may end up being avoided or ignored by others. A feeling of alienation and emptiness may result with a push to obtain more material things as a compensation for loneliness or meaninglessness, or a retreat into work as an "answer" to dealing with life's more difficult issues may result. Ask your loved ones to help you shift to "we" and "us" whenever they "catch" you too absorbed in your own stuff.

CHANGING YOUR WORLD VIEW CAN HELP YOU SHIFT BELIEFS

In cases of self-induced healing, many people report a significant change in their belief system prior to healing. Something may have happened that allowed them to see their disease not as a sentence, but as an opportunity for growth. Being bed-ridden, may allow you to write the book you never had time for, or read as you never had time to do. Rather than being beset by remorse and depression, for the first time a seemingly-ill person may be truly living.

An example of a sudden change in beliefs follows: Two battleships assigned to a training squadron had been at sea in heavy weather for several days. A seaman was serving on a lead battleship and was on watch at the bridge as night fell. The visibility was poor with patchy fog, so the captain remained on the bridge keeping an eye on all activities. Shortly after dark, the lookout on the wing of the bridge reported light bearing on the starboard bow. "Is it steady or moving astern?" the captain called out. The lookout replied, "Steady captain," which meant they were on a dangerous collision course with that ship. The captain then called to the signalman, "Signal that ship, 'we are on a collision course. Advise you change course 20 degrees'." The reply came back, "Advise you change course 20 degrees." The captain said, "Send, I'm the captain. Change course 20 degrees!" From the seaman second class came the reply, "<u>You</u> had better change course 20 degrees." By this time, the captain was furious. He spat out, "Send I'm a battleship, change course 20 degrees." Back came the flashing light, "I'm a lighthouse." The battleship changed course.

Exercise: How would your life change if you were to shift from an old belief to a new belief?

<u>Old Belief</u>	<u>New Belief</u>
My body is diseased.	My body is well, even with heart disease.
I am a victim of coronary artery disease	I am free to choose how to respond to my illness.
I did not create my own reality.	I create the reality in which I live.
Mind and body are two independent entities.	Mind and body are connected.

Or in terms we learned in Chapter 6:

<u>Seeing is believing</u>	<u>Believing is seeing</u>
I have no say in what happens	I can create wellness, joy or any

to me	experience I want. My intentions
become	my reality.
Love is something I am given air	I am surrounded by love like the
if I deserve it.	that I breathe.

Can you consider the possibility that your belief is just some conclusion that you drew based on inadequate, inaccurate and/or biased information, at a time when you were too young, immature or naive to evaluate it. If so, you might consider holding your beliefs as interim positions that you employ to maneuver through the world, subject to change with growth and additional input. Your beliefs don't own you; rather you own them in such a circumstance. Your beliefs are not facts, but instead are positions that you take at the moment. By holding your beliefs as interim positions you are not so attached to them that you would rather be right than happy, or even alive.

REFRAMING EVENTS CAN HELP YOU SHIFT BELIEFS

If you could sort life's travails into three categories, you would be better able to respond appropriately to events. For example, category one would include events that are minor, trivial and temporary, with few long-range consequences. Examples include irritation at a red light, less than perfect service from a waiter, and surliness from a salesclerk.. You could adopt the belief that minor events such as these are not worth getting upset over.

A second category includes events that are beyond your control, for example, irritation at other drivers or something said on television. You can practice letting go of your struggle for control in such situations by adopting a belief that only a foolish person would let himself remain upset at events so obviously beyond his control.

The third category involves the real, sometimes major problems that occur in family or workplace relationships. Instead of just reacting to these circumstances, believing that constructive problem-solving and good communication skills are necessary in these difficult situations will help to alleviate stress. Recognition that you have control over your reactions to difficult situations will also help.

What We Have Learned

Your beliefs affect your heart by creating stress whenever you feel threatened. "Should" statements tend to be experienced by you as threats when things don't go as you require. Anger and hostility often result. A belief that worth is dependent on accomplishment is also threatening when production lags. You can substitute positive beliefs to make it less likely that you will experience stress. You can reframe events and change your world view. Thus, it is possible for you to influence, indeed change your health by changing your mind. By recognizing that you have beliefs, you create the opportunity to identify them. You can then choose to distance yourself from limiting and harmful beliefs, and to embrace powerful, positive beliefs instead. By holding your beliefs as interim positions rather than facts, you further this process. And by perceiving you essence to be more than the beliefs you live by, more than your history, your job, or the content and form that your life has taken, you open yourself up to possibilities not available to you before. We will be discussing these possibilities in Chapter 9.

In the next chapter we will discuss the strategies that you utilize to ward off feelings of deficiency. How you misidentify yourself with your beliefs will be explored. Finally, ways to improve your self-esteem will be discussed, and the ground work for "sitting at the edge of the unknown" will be laid out.

CHAPTER 8

CHALLENGING YOUR CORE BELIEFS

If you can't get rid of the family skeleton,
you may as well make it dance.
George Bernard Shaw

We are healed of suffering only by
experiencing it in full.
Marcel Proust

Earlier, I suggested that one can view heart disease as an illness with both physical and mental components—with both physiological and cognitive aspects. A cognitive model suggests that there are common origins to the thinking patterns of individuals who later develop heart disease. When you look into the backgrounds of these individuals, you often find that many of them have experienced significant early losses in their lives which have made them vulnerable, even though they may have courageously attempted to minimize or deny the impact of these losses. Many have managed to cover up the pain of these losses by immersing themselves in achievement and productivity, but no matter how much is accomplished it may not seem enough to satisfy their own harsh internal critic.

Loss and the Heart Patient

As was mentioned previously, a parent may become unable to give time or loving attention to the child. Perhaps there was a death, a divorce, or a separation that the parent had to deal with. Alcoholism, emotional problems, arguing, job loss, economic stress, and mourning are some of the other kinds of factors which take time or loving attention away from children. In my case, my father was hospitalized often and my mother had to work full-time to support the family. This kind of situation often leads to an increase in conditional stipulations on a child, for example, "I will love you if you do such and such.", or, "When you produce, I will be available for you." What is often missing in situations where early loss occurs is unconditional acceptance of and attention to the child. Missing is this message: "I love and value you for who you are, not for what you do." The end result of this sequence is damage, perhaps severe, to the child's self-esteem.

Self-esteem and the Heart Patient

Most people have to struggle with issues of self-esteem. No one really believes that he or she is perfect in every way. But for people who later develop heart disease, low self-esteem (in the form of feelings of inadequacy, helplessness, or unlovability), is a common denominator.

To illustrate what is meant by the notion of self-esteem, imagine three plastic glasses, one labeled Type-B and two labeled Type-A. (One Type-A glass should have holes poked in the bottom). Imagine yourself pouring some water into a large measuring cup which represents the level of self-esteem. Recognize that we need to have the cup relatively full, and if it's not, we strive to fill it through a variety of ways. Now pour water into the Type-B glass and fill to over half. The Type-B now has quite a healthy amount of self-esteem. Imagine placing a funnel over the glass, and pour in more water. This represents accolades and other positive feedback that Type-B takes in, accepts, and lets increase self-esteem.

Now pour a small amount of water into the Type-A glass without holes. Many Type-A's start out with a less-healthy level of self-esteem than others. Imagine inverting a funnel over the glass, and try to pour in more water. This illustrates how Type-A individuals often reject positive feedback (even though they want it), by thoughts or statements such as, "It was nothing.", or "I could have done better.", or "I wonder what his motives are for complimenting me."

Type-A's have another problem. Imagine pouring some water into the glass with holes. Of course the water drains out, illustrating the negative self-talk or criticism of the internal critic. Now invert the funnel over the glass with holes and pour water. This combination of rejecting praise and accolades and being critical of oneself, keeps self-esteem low and generates a number of defensive strategies to raise it.

THE CORE BELIEF OF THE HEART PATIENT

A core belief is formed from the child's frequent experiences of not getting enough attention, time or unconditional love. This core belief governs much of the child's behavior for the rest of his life. The unconscious core belief is "I am inadequate." (or helpless or unlovable). To this day I go through a mental process when I meet someone new. I wonder if they think I am stupid or am somehow not worthy of respect—this from a Ph.D. in clinical psychology, with a demonstrated track record of professional and financial success. Remember that this core belief has nothing to do with reality. Your spouse may think that you are the most wonderful person in the world, but if you believe otherwise, her opinion will make no difference to your negative self-image.

The future heart patient responds to loss with predictable emotional and cognitive reactions. Emotions such as sadness and anxiety co-exist with thoughts such as "I don't have any control.", or "Nobody cares about me." If a current situation reminds you of similar circumstances in the past, all of the thoughts and feelings belonging to that earlier situation will be triggered. For example, you may be in a situation which reminds you of a time when as a child, you were alone and frightened. The core belief that you are inadequate may then be triggered, followed by thoughts such as "I don't know if I can handle this".

Many people surrender to the core belief that they are not good enough, and lead lives which reflect this belief, failing, perhaps, to achieve as they would like.. Others may attempt to escape from their inner sense of inadequacy by defense mechanisms or defensive behaviors such as being too busy to "notice" how they really feel inside. Still others have developed the strategy of counter-attack. They seem to spend their lives trying to prove to themselves and others that they are in control, accomplished and successful.

The low self-esteem which develops into a core belief is usually unconscious and must therefore be inferred from overt behaviors. There are three typical behavioral strategies that are employed to defend against the core belief:

SURRENDER

In this strategy the heart patient accepts as real the core belief that he is deficient. By surrendering to the core belief, the heart patient keeps the belief going, since he never really confronts it. An example is the person with heart disease who cannot take care of himself. He forgets to take his medications, appears confused about what he can and cannot eat, and seems unable to follow doctor's advice. Such a patient appears to have "given up" responsibility for himself, believing himself to be helpless or unlovable. In my group, one of the members often seemed confused about the homework assignments, and another had a hard time following the cardiologist's suggestions. Individuals who surrender to their core belief are often depressed and feel unappreciated. Many are "injustice collectors", monitoring the instances where they have felt cheated, abused or trodden upon, but often suffering in silence.

ESCAPE

Heart patients may use this strategy to avoid activating their core belief. For example, so as not to experience the painful effects of low self-esteem, these patients will not put themselves in situations where they could fail. They will stick to what is familiar and known, and shrink from risk. When unable to accomplish the above, they will withdraw from the field.

One member of my group equated his heart disease with being a failure. He escaped from the painful consequences of feeling like a failure by not considering himself sick . Even though admittance to the group was limited to those individuals with serious heart disease, this patient behaved as if he were auditing an interesting course, rather than participating in a program that could save his life. He used what psychologists call "denial" to cope. Another patient literally left the group whenever he was displeased with the cardiologist's attempts to get him to stop smoking and drinking. Individuals who escape from their core belief often isolate themselves from others, and have few friends or social activities. They develop ways of avoiding meaningful conversations and intimacy.

COUNTERATTACK

This is the most frequently-used strategy observed in the Type-A personalities present in my group. These individuals try to make up for their core belief by convincing themselves and others that the opposite is true. They overcompensate for feelings of low self-esteem by acquiring material wealth, prestigious positions, powerful friends, and valuable possessions. These individuals would be the last to be "accused" of not being good enough, inadequate, helpless or unlovable. But it is the driven and compensatory nature of their need to accomplish, which suggests there is more to it than meets the eye.

If you find yourself needing to prove yourself worthy of others' time and attention, or if you find yourself constantly trying to correct things or people, undo wrongs, rescue people, or overcome adversity, you may be one of those individuals who counter-attack when their self-esteem is threatened.

One individual in my group was a very successful attorney who took pride in being needed by his partners, to the point that he was actually being exploited.

Below is a hypothetical example of how cognition functions.

- *Current situation*
  You are trying to understand this complex information.
- *Automatic thoughts*
  This is really hard to understand.
  I don't know why this is important.
  I wonder if others understand this.
  I wonder what he is really up to.
  He must be a jerk (or else I am).
  I wish he would speak English.
- Core Belief
  If I don't understand this it means I'm incompetent.

If other's understand and I don't it means I'm helpless.
Unless I'm in control, master this information,
 I am vulnerable.
If I don't get it I am worthless.
No one will respect me if I don't understand this.
- Symptoms you might feel as a result:
Affective- feeling down, anxious
Motivational - Trying harder to understand or withdrawing
Cognitive - confusion, thoughts of intellectual deficiency
Physical - heart racing, agitated
Behavioral - pretending you understand, tuning out
or becoming sarcastic
- Strategy
Give up trying to understand.
Distract yourself by doing something "important".
Master the material and re-write it "correctly".

CONFRONTINGTHELIE THAT CONTROLSYOU

All of the above behaviors and strategies are based on a lie: the
child who experienced these losses is really "not good enough".
Many heart patients spend their lives under-performing because
they accept as true their core belief of inadequacy. Others lead
their lives trying to convince themselves and others that they are
not what they really are not anyway. In other words if you really
believed that you were valuable and worthwhile, you would not
have the need to prove it to yourself or others. Perfectionist
behaviors, attempts to control, and focus on task completion are
some of the ways heart patients divert themselves from the core
issues of their lives. Teaching better dietary or exercise habits
simply misses the boat, and worse, feeds into compulsive desires to
have more information and presumably achieve more control.
Perhaps the reason why heart patients have so much trouble just
being themselves is that "being" requires them to slow down long
enough that they get in touch with their feelings of low self-
esteem, inadequacy unlovability and helplessness. "Doing" and
"having" become welcome activities . Once we see that that the
core belief is not true however, there is less pressure to escape into
doing and having. The opportunity is presented for experiencing
the essential nature of who you are. With this appreciation comes
almost unlimited possibilities for growth.

You Are More Than Your Choice Of Strategy

It is as easy to misidentify yourself with the strategies that you use, as it is to mistakenly think that you are your personality, ego, roles in life, or your possessions. Many heart patients value themselves almost exclusively by what they have accomplished or accumulated. If your strategy is counterattack, there is a good chance that you will have achieved a great deal in life, providing you with "proof" that you are not deficient. If your strategy has been surrender or escape, you have less cushion to fall back on when your self-esteem is threatened. However, it is important to remember that none of these strategies addresses the underlying and fundamental questions of where your true value resides. You are so much more than what you have or have not accumulated. In a later chapter you will see that your essence is the background on which the content and form of your life appear.

Challenging Your Core Belief

Remember, the core belief of the heart patient is based on conclusions drawn very early in childhood, at a time when you could hardly be objective about what was happening to you. Because children personalize everything that happens to them, you were unable to see that your parents' inability to give you the unconditional love that you needed, was more a reflection of what was going on in their lives, than anything you did wrong or lacked. Try to get to the point where you can "forgive" your parents for whatever they were doing which took time and loving attention away from you. Of course for you get to the point where you can forgive them for their mistakes, you will have to penetrate any denial defenses that may exist that protect you from the hurt and painful feelings of the reality of your past. If you have a hard time forgiving them, try to recognize the strategy that you have been using to ward off feelings of inadequacy or low self-esteem.

Have you been surrendering to your core belief, escaping from the possibility of activating the belief, or relying upon counterattack as a defensive strategy? Recognize that these strategies are never really successful because they leave the underlying belief intact. Picture a maypole with a rope attached, so that a child would be able to swing all the way around. If the maypole is the core belief, whether you are on the left side of the maypole (surrender position), or the right side (counterattack), or whether you leave the playground altogether (escape), your core belief is still dictating your behavior. Only by acknowledging the powerful effects of the core belief, can you break free of it.

SITTING AT THE EDGE OF THE UNKNOWN

Once you have identified your strategies for dealing with your core belief, you will no longer be run by them. And if you have challenged your core belief by realizing that it is a by-product of a child's mind and not reality, then you have opened up the possibility of "being." However, a void will be created since so much of your life was taken up with your core belief and strategies of defense. The void is like sitting at the edge of the unknown, since there are no clear guideposts to orient you. Once your established and habitual patterns of thinking and behaving are questioned, identified, challenged and ultimately accepted as part of you, you will experience a sense of freedom which is at once exhilarating and frightening.

ANXIETY—HOW TO DEAL WITH THE UNKNOWN

To cope with anxiety that arises when there is uncertainty and or a lack of control, remember AWARE (*Accept, Watch, Act, Repeat, Expect)*. The key to switching out of an anxiety state is to accept it fully. Remaining in the present and accepting your anxiety causes it to disappear. To deal successfully with your anxiety, you can use the five-step AWARE strategy. By using this strategy, you will be able to accept the anxiety until it is no longer there.

1. *Accept the anxiety*. Agree to receive your anxiety. Welcome it. Say "Hello" out loud or to yourself when it appears. Say "I'll gladly accept this." Decide to be with the experience of uncertainty. Don't fight it. Replace your rejection, anger, and hatred of it with acceptance. By resisting, you are prolonging the unpleasantness of

it. Instead, flow with it and don't make it responsible for how you think, feel and act.

2. *Watch your anxiety*. Look at it without judgment, not good, not bad. Don't look at it as an unwelcome guest. Instead rate it on a 0 to 10 scale and watch it go up and down. Be with your observing self and watch the peaks and valleys of your anxiety. Be detached. Remember, you are not your anxiety. The more that you can separate yourself from the experience, the more you can just watch it. Look at your thoughts, feelings and actions as if you are a friendly but not overly-concerned bystander. Disassociate your basic self from the anxiety. In short, be *in* the anxiety state but not *of* it.

3. *Act with the anxiety*. Normalize the situation. Act as if you aren't anxious. Function with it. Slow down if you have to, but keep going. Breathe slowly and normally. If you run from the situation, your anxiety will go down, but your fear will go up. If you stay, both your anxiety and your fear will go down.

4. *Repeat the steps*. Continue to accept your anxiety. Watch it and act with it until it goes down to a comfortable level, and it will if you continue to accept, watch and act with it. Just keep repeating these three steps, accept, watch and act with it.

5. *Expect the best*. What you fear the most rarely happens. However, don't be surprised the next time you have anxiety. Instead, surprise yourself with how you handle it. As long as you are alive, you will have some anxiety. Get rid of the magical belief that you have licked anxiety for good. By accepting future anxiety, you are putting yourself in a good position to accept it when it comes again. Sitting at the edge of the unknown, creates excitement as well as anxiety. Be curious.

THE BENEFITS OF UNCERTAINTY

Human beings seem to like certainty, predictability, order and control. Many of us devote our lives to sameness, habit and familiarity as a source of stability and comfort. At the same time however, there appears to be a need for stimulation, novelty, change and adventure. How do we reconcile these two aspects of ourselves? It is important to accept these two sides as normal and valuable. Without a certain amount of stability, a child would never venture away from his or her mother. Without a certain degree of sanity, an artist could never dip into the wellspring of his creativity for inspiration.

Without risk, there is no excitement, no growth and no creation of new things. Therefore it is necessary for us to accept our fear and go beyond what is known. The problem with certainty is that it leads to boredom, stagnation, decay, and resignation. The benefits of uncertainty are that life will move forward, and evolve into something new and enlivening.

Individuals with heart disease have experienced losses in their lives which have left them frightened and vulnerable. Rigidly clinging to habits, focusing upon the "correct" ways of doing things, and seeking information as protection from the unknown (rather than because of enthusiasm and interest), are some of the ways in which individuals with heart disease attempt to deal with their perceived sense of vulnerability. It is time to recognize that the patterns of behavior used to protect against uncertainty have created havoc with health and well-being. It is far better to welcome change and uncertainty with an adventurous spirit and a trust in the universe.

What We Have Learned

Heart patients often have a history of early loss which triggers certain predictable patterns of thinking and feeling. Because of personal problems, a parent may be unable to give time or loving attention to the child. The child learns to value himself more for what he produces than for just being himself. He develops a self concept of "not being good enough", and his self-esteem suffers. Over time, a core belief is established which determines much of the thinking, feeling and behavior of the future heart patient. This unconscious core belief is "I am helpless", or "I am unlovable." Because of the unpleasant nature of this belief, strategies are chosen to defend against it. The person may surrender to the belief that he is not good enough, and perhaps never achieve much in life. He may escape from the belief by busying himself with activities, or he can counterattack. In this last strategy, the heart patient may spend his life trying to prove to himself and others that he is in control, accomplished and successful. These behaviors and strategies are based on a lie however—that the child who experienced a lack of unconditional positive regard is really "not good enough". It is important to realize that this early loss was not a function of anything that the child did, but rather a reflection of parental circumstances. By forgiving your parents, recognizing the strategies that you use to defend against your erroneous core belief, and accepting the anxiety that comes with sailing in unknown waters, you open yourself up to new possibilities in "being". Sitting at the edge of the unknown, embracing uncertainty, your life can move forward into health and well-being.

CHAPTER 9

ANGER, DEPRESSION AND HEART DISEASE

*Anybody can become angry—but to become angry
with the right person, and to the right degree, and
at the right time, and for the right purpose, and in
the right way—that is not within everyone's power,
and is not easy.*
                                                    Aristotle

Negative emotions, like anger and depression have definite effects on people who develop heart disease. In previous chapters, I talked about the Type-A personality, characterized by a sense of time urgency, free floating hostility, and an intense drive for achievement. Also, in Chapter 7, I presented a model of heart disease, in which childhood experiences of loss resulted in feelings of low self-esteem and a core belief of inadequacy. Strategies to defend against the core belief include *surrender, escape and counterattack*. Individuals who surrender, subject themselves to continued feelings of depression, since they essentially endorse beliefs of helplessness or worthlessness. People who seek to escape from their core belief, become increasingly anxious as they attempt to insure that the environment is free of risk, uncertainty and threats to their precarious sense of self-esteem. Those individuals who counterattack, experience unhealthy amounts of anger as they seek to achieve more and more in less and less time, and to control circumstances that are essentially outside their control.

THE MAIN CAUSES OF ANGER IN THE HEART PATIENT

Anger is often related to an individual's level of self-esteem. When self-esteem is threatened, anger is often the result. Thus, if you feel attacked, diminished or put down, it is likely that you will experience anger. Since individuals with heart disease often have negative beliefs about themselves, they are more likely to experience threat than most other people. For example, imagine someone walking down the street who meets a young child. The child suddenly sticks out his tongue and says "You are stupid because you can't add numbers and I can." An individual with high self-esteem might regard the child with amusement or interest, but would not take what was said personally or feel attacked. If the individual had low self-esteem, however, he might actually question himself and perhaps even argue in a defensive manner with the child.

A second major cause of anger has to do with unmet expectations. Whenever you believe that things should be a certain way, and they turn out to be different, anger may be the result. For example, you thought that your boss would give you a raise only to find out that your pay check will remain the same. You might get angry at your boss for not fulfilling your expectations. "Injustice collectors" are often angry for exactly the same reason. These individuals believe that they are mistreated, and that they should have been treated differently.

The third major cause of anger involves a perceived loss of control. Situations which evoke unwelcome and painful emotions such as fear or frustration are often seen as occurring outside of one's control. For example, you are driving along when suddenly a car passes you dangerously on the right-hand side. You have no control over what happened, nor do you experience having any control over your racing heartbeat. You become angry because of your perceived lack of control. Another example might be found with a teenager who can't seem to pick up after himself, no matter how many times you have reminded him. You seemingly have no control over the teenager's behavior and become frustrated and angry.

ARE YOU AN ANGRY PERSON?

To gain a general impression of how you measure up in the area of free floating anger, please answer the following questions.

- When an elevator doesn't come as quickly as it should in your opinion, do your thoughts focus on the inconsiderate or incompetent people responsible for the delay?
- Do you frequently check up on family members or co-workers to make sure they haven't made a mistake in some tasks?
- Do you sense your heart pounding or your breath quickening when you find yourself in a slow line in traffic or at the bank or supermarket?
- When little things go wrong, do you often feel like lashing out at the world?
- When someone criticizes you, do you quickly begin to feel annoyed?
- Do you frequently look for opportunities to pay people back for mistreating you?
- Do you frequently find yourself muttering at the television when you hear something that you dislike?
- If an elevator stops too long on the floor above you, are you likely to pound on the door, stomp your feet, or clench your fist?
- When in the supermarket express line, do you often count the items in the baskets of people ahead of you to be sure that they are not over the limit?

If you answered "yes" to at least four questions, the chances are that your level of free-floating anger is too high.

THE CONNECTION BETWEEN ANGER AND HEART DISEASE

There have been many studies which show that individuals with high levels of hostility have greater risks of heart disease and premature death. For example, Dr. Daniel Ford at Johns Hopkins School of Medicine states that medical students with high levels of anger have twice the risk of developing depression and two to three times the risk of having a heart attack, as do other students. It is not known exactly how arteries build up plaque under conditions of anger, but it is likely that higher levels of adrenaline accelerate the formation of blockages. And of course it is well known that angry individuals who are ready to "fight" on a moment's notice, secrete more adrenaline.

In a study of 1305 men in Boston without known heart disease, researchers at Harvard University found that after seven years, those individuals with a high degree of anger had about triple the risk of coronary disease compared than people with low-anger.

RECOGNIZE WHEN YOU ARE ANGRY

Many individuals with Type-A behavior patterns have lost their ability to be aware of what is going on inside them. In their efforts to please or impress others, and to protect themselves from threats to their self-esteem, these individuals have often ignored their own feelings. Insecurity, exhaustion, loneliness, irritation, impatience, aggravation, and anger are some of the internal feelings that may have become inaccessible. As a result, it is important to learn the signs that indicate the presence of these hidden feelings. Ask your loved ones to help you by pointing out when you are behaving in a sarcastic or hyper-critical manner. Similarly, ask to be made aware of times when you are grimacing, teasing or laughing in an explosive or unsettling way.

Since Type-A anger often arises from an excessive sense of entitlement or self-absorption, it is important that you ask loved ones to point out when you are being overly demanding. Ask to be made aware of excessive use of the words "I", "me", and "my".

A particularly dangerous situation arises with individuals who are highly-conscientious and quite concerned about fitting in, being liked and appearing in a positive light. These individuals face a problem when they get angry because they view anger as socially undesirable. The suppression, repression or denial of anger in these individuals has been associated with increased risk of heart disease.

It would be better for these individuals to allow themselves the experience of anger, to be able to admit to others that they are angry from time to time, and to discover that most normal people can accept and even love them, despite their occasional bouts of anger.

How to Handle Your Anger

Although anger is naturally-occurring and often a healthy response to threat or frustration, when it occurs too frequently, is too intense or lasts too long, anger becomes dangerous to health and well-being. Individuals sometimes become addicted to anger because the accompanying physiological arousal energizes them. This abuse of anger is also unhealthy. While the experience of anger in the above circumstances is unhealthy, it is also important that if anger arises, it not be denied or suppressed in an effort to appear reasonable and in control.

The experience of anger can be reduced in frequency and intensity by changing how you think. We saw in a previous chapter that eliminating the word "should" from your vocabulary, could be beneficial. Substitute the word "could" whenever possible. For example, "He *should* have given me a bonus", would be a thought that could easily trigger anger in the event of a disappointment. Changing the sentence to read "He *could* have given me a bonus", opens up the possibilities of different outcomes in the event of a disappointment. The use of "could" implies that there is more to the story.

Perhaps you would have received a bonus if the company had had a better year, or if you had done a better job, or your boss was a progressive and well-trained manager. The use of the word "could" allows you to reason with yourself and reduce your level of anger.

Since threats to your self-esteem trigger anger, anything that you do to strengthen your self-image will reduce your vulnerability to anger. Realizing that your self-esteem is based on an erroneous core belief formed in childhood, will set the stage for re-examination and challenge. In Chapter 10, you will begin to recognize that the essence of who you are is pure potential. This will free you from the conditioning of the past, and allow you to choose how you wish to react in any given situation. Anger can be a *choice*, and not necessarily an automatic reaction.

Accept that there are situations which are outside your control. It takes wisdom to "go with the flow", and accept what you cannot change. Fear and frustration don't necessarily have to lead to anger. You can use fear constructively to prepare yourself better for the next circumstance in which fear typically arises, such as giving a lecture before an audience. You could take defensive-driving classes so as to become less fearful on the road.

Nor does frustration necessarily have to lead to anger. You could increase frustration tolerance by re-framing the situation, as for example, by telling yourself that your teenager's messiness is good training for becoming less compulsive or rigid. You could also allow your frustration to motivate you toward seeking help, rather than getting angry.

ANGER AND WOMEN

Cardiovascular disease is the leading cause of death in women in the U.S., accounting for half of all deaths of women age 50 and over. Much of what may be said about men cardiac patients is also true of women, but there are some differences. Women tend to be cardiac "reactors", responding with larger increases in heart rate than men when exposed to stressful tasks. Antagonistic (disagreeable, manipulative) behavior and cynical hostility, but not overt aggression, are found to be related to cardiovascular reactivity in women.

Our culture reinforces less overt expression of anger in women. It is important for women to give themselves permission to get angry, and to allow themselves to express the anger directly. Too often, women are concerned that they will not be accepted or loved unless they behave in agreeable or polite ways. This forces them to express their anger in disguised or subtle forms, which often results in negative consequences for the patient as well as her relationships.

Some studies have shown that women tend to be more vulnerable to life's events. It appears that there is an emotional cost to the natural caring of women, thus they may have higher stress levels. In addition, the dual roles which many women play in our culture—mother/executive, wife/care giver, worker/housewife—appear to exacerbate stress. While women share many of the predictors for cardiovascular disease with men, there are additional ones for women. Low education levels, excess stress, and lack of vacations are implicated in heart disease in women. Women who work in the home, who have difficulty falling asleep, or do excessive amounts of grueling housework seem to have elevated levels of heart disease. In a 1993 study by Higgins and Thom, it was found that while women had more physician visits for heart disease than men, fewer were hospitalized, and more died of their disease.

WHAT TO DO IF YOU FIND YOURSELF ANGRY

Is it better to express the anger you already feel, or to hold it in? Research suggests that if you express your anger, you are likely to experience even more anger. Whereas if you keep anger in, you are likely to experience other negative consequences, such as depression or headaches. It is probably better to express anger verbally, rather than physically, and better to express your feelings in an articulate manner than to curse and scream. However, it is best to remain flexible, so that you can adapt your behavior to the circumstances.

Sometimes, it may be better to let off steam in a direct, non-violent, assertive manner, whereas at other times holding your anger in may be safer and less damaging to your relationships, and to your heart. Some people, afraid of their anger, act prematurely to try to get rid of it by ventilating or suppressing. It is better to take note of your anger, locate how it expresses itself in your body, and watch it dissipate. This will take you out of your mind and into your body, quickening the reduction of anger.

TIPS FOR BECOMING LESS ANGRY

- Exercise regularly.
- Learn to laugh at yourself.
- Allow yourself to cry when you feel sad or frightened.
- Try to put yourself in others' shoes whenever possible.
- Whenever you hear yourself think or say hostile thoughts, yell to yourself "Stop!"
- Tell your friends and loved ones that you need their help in trying to reduce your inappropriate level of anger.
- Try to reason with yourself whenever you are angry. How could things be seen differently?
- Try to paraphrase what others say rather than offering your own opinions.
- Volunteer to help others less fortunate.
- Learn to forgive others when you feel mistreated.
- Become more involved with the teachings of your church.

- Get a pet.
- Do something with a friend at least once weekly.
- Learn how to meditate or relax and use this skill whenever you are angry.
- Try to distract yourself when you get angry. Turn on the radio while in a traffic jam; read a magazine while standing in line.
- Learn the difference between being appropriately assertive, and aggressive.
- Pretend that this day is your last. Your anger will seem less important.
- Get in touch with the natural beauty around you. Take a walk on the beach or in the woods.
- Increase your self-esteem by learning a new skill. Take a course at school or by mail.
- Decrease your wants and needs. Simple pleasures are often more meaningful and enduring.
- Practice smiling.
- Routinely review your successes and your qualities and talents responsible for those successes.
- Avoid being critical of yourself for lack of perfection.
- Stop "shoulding" all over the place. Use of the word "should" can be dangerous to your health.
- Use other yardsticks besides accomplishments to measure yourself.
- Recall pleasant memories for ten minutes.
- Try to eliminate words such as "I", "me", and "mine"
- Verbalize affection to friends and family members.

DEPRESSION AND HEART DISEASE

In a previous chapter we learned that a large percentage of individuals who later develop heart disease experienced early losses in their lives. These experiences made them vulnerable to later experiences of loss such as divorce, relocation, death of a loved one or job insecurity. We saw that children who grow up in homes where one or both parents are emotionally or physically unavailable, develop a core belief that they are inadequate, in part to explain the lack of unconditional love that they experience. We made the assertion that when parents who, because of their own problems, are unable to sensitively respond to the heartfelt needs of their child, the child experiences the lack of unconditional love as an attack on the heart. A person who is neglected by parents during childhood may come to believe that he caused and deserved the neglect, and may find it hard to believe that he is lovable in adulthood.

Similarly, someone who was attended to by a parent only when he was serving the needs of the parent, may come to the conclusion that it is important to be attuned to other's problems, even to his own detriment. In both cases, vital supplies to the emotional heart are cut off.

We discussed how many of these children "surrender" to their core belief that they are inadequate in some way. By accepting as true the core belief that he or she is helpless or unlovable, the child subjects himself to feelings of depression. And by surrendering to the belief, there is little opportunity to find evidence of the inaccuracy of the belief, since lives become constricted, risks are avoided, and challenges are seen as too insurmountable to face.

A number of other individuals who later develop heart disease attempt to counter their core belief by compulsive achievement striving, as if to say to themselves and the world that they are not helpless or inadequate. As long as the Type-A individual is engaged in productive activities, he is protected from the awareness of his core belief and his underlying depression. When such activities cease, such as after a loss of a job or health, the depression is unmasked. It is may be that depression occurs because the individual, angry at the experience of loss, turns his anger inward.

Just as arousal is the body's response to stress, withdrawal is the response to loss. Bodily processes slow down, energy is sapped, replaced by fatigue and lethargy. Sleep is disturbed, and appetite is altered. Sexual performance and bowel function slow down as well. While all people experience loss and disappointment, in response to setbacks at work, broken relationships, or deaths of friends and relatives, most people can get over the pain of loss after an appropriate period of mourning or bereavement. Individuals who experienced the pain of early loss, are less able to handle later losses. They walk around with a chronic sense of sorrow which is easily triggered by thoughts rather than real losses. And when real losses occur there is an exaggerated and prolonged response.

These individuals attempt to escape the pain of loss by withdrawal into themselves, denying or avoiding anything that would remind them of the painful situation, distracting themselves, isolating themselves from needed supports, and by so doing, set the stage for additional heartache and depression. *There is evidence to suggest that depression is a risk factor for heart attack. And there is data to suggest that individuals who deny that they are depressed, are at increased risk for heart disease.*

It stands to reason that an individual whose lifestyle is drastically altered by the presence of heart disease would mourn the loss of his pre-morbid state, unable to do what was easily accomplished before the onset of disease. Less obvious, is the idea that undiagnosed depression may contribute to the development of heart disease in the first place. It could be easily argued that most children experience hardships in childhood, but not all of them develop heart disease. Still, so many individuals do develop heart disease, that it is just as conceivable to implicate undiagnosed depression as a risk factor as it is to consider the damaging effects of poor nutrition and lack of exercise. It has been estimated that 7 to 14 percent of children will experience an episode of major depression before the age of 15. In a study by J. Kaufman, 25 percent of maltreated children met the criteria for depression. Another study by R.D. Todd found that depressed children had families which were two to three times more likely than controls to have a history of alcoholism.

New evidence that depression leads to heart disease comes from Dr. William Eaton of the Johns Hopkins School of Hygiene and Public Health in Baltimore. Dr. Eaton found that individuals who were free of heart disease in 1981, were four times more likely to have a heart attack in the next fourteen years if they were depressed.

The mechanisms by which depression may lead to heart disease are speculative, although there is evidence that the increased levels of hormonal activity in depressed individuals could promote dangerous arrhymthias and suppress the immune system. Although depressed individuals feel sad and lethargic, they are usually in a state of hyperarousal. They sleep less or wake early, lose their appetite, reduce sexual activity and seem to be mobilized for fight or flight. Their blood contains stress hormones that are 30 percent higher than those of people who are not depressed, according to Dr. Richard Veith, a professor of psychiatry at the University of Washington.

Depressed individuals, bereft of joy or pleasure, neglect their health and show an increase in behaviors such as smoking, alcohol consumption, and poor diet. There is the suggestion that a reduction in serotonin in the central nervous system, as occurs in depressed and hostile individuals, could be responsible for many of the effects observed in individuals who develop heart disease.

Are you depressed? Ask yourself these questions:
- Do you feel sad or empty, or get tearful most of the day, nearly every day?
- Are you significantly less interested in doing things most of the day, nearly every day?
- Have you lost or gained a significant amount of weight without trying during the last month?
- Do you find it hard to sleep or sleep too much on a daily basis?
- Do you feel restless or agitated every day, or feel lethargic and slowed down?
- Are you fatigued, and have little energy most days?
- Do you have feelings of worthlessness or excessive guilt nearly every day?
- Do you find it hard to think or concentrate or make decisions nearly every day?
- Do you find yourself thinking about death or suicide often?

If you answered "yes" to at least five questions, then there is an excellent chance that you are experiencing depression severe enough to warrant a visit to your physician.

WHAT YOU CAN DO TO HELP YOUR DEPRESSION

- Get in touch with your core belief of inadequacy, and dispute it.
- See your doctor to discuss possible medications.
- Pay attention to the small things in life that make you smile or laugh.
- Make a collection of things that give you pride or pleasure—pictures of your kids or pets, awards, souvenirs of trips you enjoyed.
- Travel to a favorite place.
- Consider getting a pet. Research has shown that pet owners experience reduced stress, and that pets can help overcome depression.
- Join a support group for heart patients.
- Volunteer your time. Helping others can be therapeutic for you also.

WHAT WE HAVE LEARNED

Heart patients have a core, unconscious belief that they are inadequate. Anger often results when their self-esteem is threatened, when expectations are unmet, or when there is a perceived lack of control. You may have a reservoir of free-floating anger which can impact upon your heart, according to research findings. Learning to recognize and deal with your anger can be lifesaving. Changing your thoughts, increasing your self-esteem, learning to accept situations which are outside your control, and increasing your tolerance for frustration can all help you to reduce your levels of anger.

Learning to recognize depression is also important to your well-being. Undiagnosed depression is a risk factor for heart disease. Depression may begin in early life. The core belief of inadequacy formed in response to parental unavailability is an inaccurate conclusion based on childhood perceptions. You are much more than the strategies you have adopted to defend yourself against your core belief, as will be seen in the next chapter. There are many things that you can do to fight depression including disputing your core belief, volunteering, and joining a support group.

CHAPTER 10

THE ESSENTIAL YOU

*If we have not quiet in our minds, outward comfort will do
no more than a golden slipper on a gouty foot.*
John Bunyan

*Each of us is meant to have a character all our own, to be what
no other can exactly be, and do what no other can exactly do."*
William Ellery Channing

In Chapter 6, we learned that beliefs are important because
they help to guide you through life, but can also affect your health,
and limit what is possible for you. You learned that you are often
unaware of your beliefs and are therefore vulnerable to stress. For
example, you may be angry that a driver stopped suddenly without
warning, and yet be unaware that your beliefs about how people
should behave may be the cause of your anger, not the driver. You
also learned that heart patients often have an unconscious core
belief that they are inadequate or unlovable, and that they often
use strategies such as counterattack to defend against their
erroneous core beliefs. While your beliefs seem like facts to you, I
stated that they are suspect because the perceptions that they rest
upon are often inaccurate. Your motivation and needs affect your
perceptions, you influence what appears before you, you respond
to major but not gradual changes, and you listen "for"
confirmation of your point of view rather than "to" the speaker.

Furthermore, many beliefs are based on thinking errors such as "all-or-none thinking" and "overgeneralization".

Yet despite the above, it is difficult to overcome the seductiveness of believing in conventional ways, so important is it for you to fit in. Besides, your beliefs are like water to the fish, so familiar to you that you hardly know that there is anything there. I mentioned that perhaps the best that you can do is to hold your beliefs not as facts but as interim positions, useful in navigating through life, but not necessarily written in stone. And earlier I alluded to the possibility that you may be more than the beliefs you live by, your history, your job, and the content and form that your life has taken. This chapter is about the essence of who you are.

DISTRACTING YOURSELF FROM PAINFUL REALITIES

There is a peculiar quality that we share, namely an ability to focus our attention to the degree that all else is obliterated. This ability has positive and negative effects. For the baseball player, it helps to focus concentration on the ball to the point that it appears to slow down and to be bigger than it is. In India, people have been known to focus their attention such that they could walk barefoot on hot coals and to lie naked on nails without being hurt. The intense focus protects against potentially-threatening realities, such as being struck out at the plate, or being burned or impaled. A religious person may focus on her rosary beads during difficult or painful times, while someone in a bad relationship may focus on his work to distract himself from the painful effects of his unmet needs and expectations. A person may focus on obtaining symbols of success and happiness, such as cars, and other material possessions in order to distract himself from feelings of loneliness, separation or emptiness. Of course the distraction postpones the solution to his problems. The same effect occurs when you "get into a rut", finding yourself doing the same things over and over again. Thus, *both habit and diversion can serve the same function of screening you from painful realities.*

There is a reality that we all face which is extremely painful, namely the inevitability of our own demise. Our culture attempts to protect us from this inevitability by offering us religious notions of life after death. More subtly, we agree to "soften" unpleasant reminders of our impermanence by our use of language ("He passed away.", "We put our dog to sleep.") Dying occurs primarily in hospitals which are relatively out of sight. We use every available tool to retard signs of aging, from hair color to plastic surgery. *We distract ourselves from our painful existential dilemma by focusing upon acquiring wealth, power and control, and by anaesthetizing ourselves through habit.*

Did you ever say to yourself "That's just not me.", when someone asks you to do something that's inconsistent with how you view yourself? For example, someone asks you for a hug and you don't do hugs. Or you're asked if you would say a few words on behalf of someone at a gathering, and you shy away from the opportunity ("I'm not good at speeches," you say to yourself). Some of us may be quite proud of our declarations as to what is and is not you. And others may feel a little uncomfortable, as though an opportunity was lost. Or perhaps you harbor a vague wish that you were "different." How we define ourselves to ourselves, who we say we are, is critical to our health and well-being. Our self-image creates and limits what's possible for us ("I don't do......, "That's not me."). In other words we behave in ways which are consistent with our self-definitions.

Did you ever notice that our self-definition is held onto like life itself, as if to abandon it would leave us invisible, without an identity, an amorphous blob? Consider that many people would sooner die than do something that goes against their view of themselves. What is it that keeps us so bound to our limited self-definitions?

It is fear. Fear of the unknown, fear of what others think of us, fear of our own potential. What if someone were desperately clutching a life raft for fear of drowning, but was in the middle of a shopping center parking lot. We would think that was pretty silly. Yet we defend our narrow definitions of ourselves as if our security rested in defense rather than elsewhere. Maybe identification with, attachment to, and openness to others is a better source of security. People are often threatened by intolerant or closed people and approach warmly those who are most open or tolerant.

YOUR SENSE OF WHO YOU ARE

Exercise: Imagine yourself at a gathering of people. Someone next to you strikes up a conversation by saying, "Hi, I'm Mary,. Tell me about yourself". What would you say to her? Take a minute or two to think about your response.

If you are like most people in our culture, you would begin by stating your name. You would probably talk about where you live, now or in the past. You might mention what you do for a living, and what other roles in life you have, for example, husband or father. You might describe yourself further by talking about some of your interests or hobbies. If the conversation continues, you might even have the opportunity to share your "story", a brief and well-rehearsed narrative of your life.

Most of us would agree that the above offers a pretty good description of the self. *The sum total of your social roles, interests, beliefs, hobbies, and job description define who you take yourself to be.* For our purposes, whether you call the above your <u>self</u>, your <u>personality</u>, your <u>identity</u>, your <u>social mask</u>, or your <u>ego</u> is immaterial. The main point is that *your <u>self</u> is an abstraction composed of attributions and interpretations formed in the past.* Once formed, your identity is held onto like life itself.

You strive to be consistent with who you take yourself to be, even it means depriving yourself of new experiences and opportunities. For example, you may be invited to an interesting party, but at the last minute. If you have decided that you are a person who is somewhat shy and not at all spontaneous, you would reject the invitation, telling yourself that you need more notice, and maybe even interpreting the late invitation as a slap in the face, justifying your anger. Because you were unwilling to see the invitation as merely an event, devoid of meaning, you may have missed the opportunity to have fun.

YOUR STORY ABOUT YOURSELF

Most of us have a story or life script which can be encapsulated in two or three paragraphs. My story would appear as follows: "I was raised in a working-class town, the son of a disabled war veteran who was always sick. We had very little money, and only one can of soup had to feed four faces. The neighbors helped to raise me, since my mother had to work to support the family. Once, the neighbors chipped in and sent me to a summer camp for underprivileged children. The family overcame great odds. My father eventually went to college late in life, despite being 100%

disabled according to Uncle Sam. We eventually relocated to a better neighborhood. My father was harsh and abusive because of his illness, but later softened up. My mother was a "saint" for putting up with such hardships."

Versions of this story of my life have been repeated hundreds of times to anyone who would listen. It seems very real to me, just as my beliefs seem like facts to me. The story is perhaps unconsciously designed to elicit a certain amount of sympathy, but also tells the listener that I am from a family of fighters, and by extension that I am a force to be reckoned with.

The problem with this narrative of my life, and any narrative, is that 1) it can define my life, and 2) the story is untrue. My life became an extension of the drama as I had envisioned it.

I developed two different themes from the story above, "Poor Larry" and "King Larry", the latter role most likely a defense against the former role. Unconsciously, "Poor Larry" would elicit sympathy by attempting to make people think of me as helpless or a victim of various events, people, circumstances, or illness. "King Larry" would expect others to do all kinds of things for me, without proper compensation or gratitude. These roles, have been played out over a lifetime, until I was able to understand their origins in my story. Most importantly, I see my heart disease as having been influenced by these two roles.

In general, whenever present circumstances remind you of your story, you will rekindle all of the emotions and thoughts that occurred during the time that the story developed. For example, in my situation if my wife worked late one night, I would experience her absence as similar to when I was a child and my mother had to work. All the emotions of being alone, and "abandoned", would come out as if I were still the child. The "Poor Larry" role would be set in motion by the feelings of abandonment. And King Larry would appear, feeling entitled to "just compensation" for Poor Larry's hardships. Perhaps he would order a chocolate sundae or two.

The King arrogantly consumes his "just desserts", commanding along the way that no ill effects shall result from his actions (such as weight gain) or if they do, he will handle it later. Thus, my arrogance and sense of entitlement kept me from eating in a sane manner, while allowing me to get the substitute-gratification I craved.

What was needed was a third role, which didn't come from my story or narrative. I have lately created such a role for myself—

Citizen Larry. Citizen Larry is neither superior nor inferior to others; he is just a member of the most exciting group that exists, the community of human beings. Now when triggered by a current circumstance reminiscent of my story, if I am able to get enough distance from the story to diminish its hold on me, (I will discuss how to do this later), I ask myself how Citizen Larry would handle the circumstance. I remind myself that no self-respecting citizen would allow himself to "pig out", because he would have too much respect for his body.

The difficult reality is that your "story", which seems so true and realistic is, in fact, false. You need to realize that the story is composed of interpretations of events, rather than the events themselves. A brief digression into the nature of reality is necessary in order to appreciate this distinction.

THREE DIMENSIONS OF REALITY

- *Cultural reality.* This is the form of reality whereby we obtain a consensus of opinions and call that agreement "reality." For example, we agree that we should stop at red lights, pay our taxes, send our kids to school, and be polite to others. We create laws which allow us to "own" property and other possessions. Many of our cultural realities become incorporated into our belief systems, such as "You have to work hard to make a good living." We rarely question these cultural beliefs, even though there are people living in different cultures who may question these "realities".
- *Physical reality.* This is the reality that is physical and tangible. It is about what happens or what is, without story, drama or agreement. You can measure physical reality, since it has distance, time and form as components. For example, a chair is solid, has dimensions, exists now, and is located in a particular place. "My father was hospitalized several times," is a statement of physical reality.
- *The unreal.* This area of reality covers over physical reality. Our fantasies, expectations, core beliefs, meanings, shoulds and have-to's, are superimposed upon what really happened. "We had to make do without my father who had to be hospitalized several times," is a statement that expands upon physical reality, to include feelings about his absence, ("We had to make do...") and the circumstances of his hospitalization, (He

had to be hospitalized again...") Most of us live with no distinction between what happened and our story or drama about what happened. Thus our story seems like reality to us, not an interpretation.

HOW TO REWRITE YOUR STORY SO THAT IT NO LONGER RUNS YOU..

Exercise. Rewrite your story from the point of view of physical reality. For example, to take the drama out of my story, I would rewrite it in the following way.

I am the son of a father who was frequently ill. We lived in a neighborhood, with lots of kids and neighbors. I ate dinner at my friends house frequently. My grandmother and aunt lived with us for several years. The family lived on income from the government, supplemented by my grandmother's contributions, and my mother's job. Later, as my father began to recover, he went to college, became a psychologist, and relocated the family to a large single house. As he progressed in school, my father became more approachable. My mother had many fine qualities and some not-so-fine qualities."

This story captures more of the reality of the situation, rather than the drama, from which my identity took shape. It would be hard to derive a King Larry or Poor Larry theme from a story devoid of interpretation and drama.

To rid yourself of the effects of your story, it would also be very helpful if you rewrote it again, but this time from the point of view of yourself as a victim. For example, I might start the story this way: "My father never played ball with me. I never had enough money to buy things like my friends. My friends were better off than I was."

Then do it again from the point of view of yourself as a character in a tragedy. For example: "My father was a handsome young man who was struck down by a disabling illness in the prime of his life. The family was forced to live on government subsidies and contributions from neighbors." The story can be repeated again as if you were in a comedy, and again as if you were a hero. The more drama you can put into the story, the sooner it will begin to look absurd to you. You will find that the story will begin to disappear as a major influence in your life, and that you will be free to create your life anew.

Now you should have a finer appreciation of what I meant above, when I suggested that *the narrative or story of your life, which seems so real to you and in fact determines a great deal of what you do in life, is based upon interpretations and cultural conditioning, rather than reality.*

YOUR PERSONALITY AS A SOURCE OF DISTRACTION

By far, the greatest source of distraction and deception is your focus upon yourself, or ego, as a buttress against impermanence. It is as if you can tell yourself "Jobs, spouses, friends, can come and go, but at least I have myself, my memories, and my identity". You believe that you have a solid identity which you own like your material possessions. It is composed of your memories, job description, and roles in life. While seemingly comforting and protective, your identity may actually be limiting and counter-productive to your health and well-being.

In a previous chapter I pointed out how you could devote your life to proving that you are not inadequate or unlovable, an erroneous belief that you may have formed as a child. In a similar fashion, *your attachment to your identity or self-image may actually retard your ability to experience life, be healthy, relate to others, and be in touch with your spirituality.* Ironically, by focusing on yourself, you may be distracting yourself from a fear of impermanence that may not exist. Maybe your "ownership" of your self is an illusion to distract yourself from what isn't true anyway, namely, that you are separate and impermanent.

If you had the perceptual capacity to see what was happening at the sub-atomic level, you would find that your body, reduced to its essential state, is a bundle of energy and information in a universe of energy and information. Your body is not separate from the body of the universe because at the quantum level there are no well-defined edges. Thus your attachment to yourself, your personality or ego, is based on fear and insecurity—the illusion that you are impermanent and alone in the universe. Your search for security by "owning" more things, controlling more people, achieving more and more, is based on this illusion.

But ask yourself, "What is there to fear?", knowing that you are connected to the universal flow of energy and information. The concept of impermanence loses meaning once this is understood. You need not hold onto your ego or personality as a defense against your eventual demise. If in fact, you are like other forms of energy and information, you will exist forever.

YOUR ESSENCE

Exercise: Pick a quiet and relaxing spot. Close your eyes after reading the instructions in order to help you to focus inside. Try to get in touch with your most basic and personal "I", as it appears in the sentence "I am resting comfortably". See if you can determine the root of the "I" feeling. It may help to repeat silently to yourself the sentence "I am resting comfortably." a few times.

Did you notice that you could observe yourself silently speaking the above sentence? Who is it that hears the sentence? Are you the "I" that speaks the sentence, the "I" that hears the sentence, or the "I" that experiences "resting comfortably", or all of the above?

You will find that it is easy to access the contents of your mind. For example, you can think, "I am resting comfortably.", but it is impossible to put your finger on the "I" that observes or hears the sentence. Every time you try to observe the observing "I", it seems to jump under cover. If the "I" who is looking or hearing could be observed, you would be able to describe it. *The reason it can't be observed is that the innermost "I" is the observer or witness, not that which can be observed. This innermost "I" can be experienced but not seen.*

Exercise: After reading the instructions, shut your eyes. Try to be aware of what is going on. You may hear certain sounds, or see spots in front of your eyes. You may observe thoughts that come and go, memories may crop up, desires and fantasies may appear and disappear. All the time however, you will notice that your awareness stays constant.

Now try to observe awareness. You will find the same difficulties that occurred when trying to observe your innermost "I". Awareness cannot be made an object of observation any more

than your innermost "I" can be observed. This is because awareness
is the very means whereby you can observe. Awareness is of a
different nature than the contents of the mind. It is featureless and
goes beyond thoughts, sensations, and emotions.

*Thus both "I" and awareness are one and the same. We cannot
observe either one because both give rise to what is observed. Both
are fundamental to experience. We know the internal observer not
by observing it, but by being it. I am awareness and that is my
essence. The essential state is pure awareness or consciousness.* In
that state everything is possible, as we are pure potential. Your
essence is beyond any individual identification, such as your name
or profession. It is beyond form, such as your appearance or
clothing. It is beyond process, such as your attempts to deal with
heart disease or family issues. And it is beyond your beliefs . Your
essence gives rise to the above. Your essence is not your position
or point of view; rather it is space or context in which all of your
points of view occur. No <u>actual</u> thing, your essence is the space of
things. It contains the screen of life, but never appears on it. Your
essence is the context of all contexts. Your essence is complete.
Working from your essence rather than your personality, ego or
self, allows for natural creativity, happiness, health and well-being.
I realize that this may be the most difficult concept I have
presented in this book. But I believe that mastery of this idea is
key to well-being.

So what is it that prevents you from operating out of this state
of being? I will discuss this below.

WHY WE RESIST BEING OUR ESSENCE

The major barrier to "being", is a preoccupation with "doing"
and "having", as I discussed in an earlier chapter. Above, I discussed
how easy it is to be run by your story, which of course is another
barrier to being your essence. *It is dizzying and disorienting to
conceive of yourself as a space of pure possibility for a number of
other reasons.*

First, you have spent a lifetime building an identity that you
are quite attached to. You may feel that you would have worked
hard "for nothing" if you were asked to recognize that your
identity is not important or even accurate. After all, people will
kill to preserve their sense of identity, and will agree to be killed
rather than renounce their beliefs or ideas about who they are.

Second, whatever you have gained in life—accomplishments, love, possessions—you may believe came through your unique personality and identity. It is hard to consider the notion that these gains came to you despite your attachment to your identity and beliefs.

Third, it is frightening to conceive of the idea that you have the power to create your life in any direction. To believe this requires that you realize also that you may have created things you are not pleased about or proud of in your life, such as disease, divorce, or problems with your children. This power requires responsibility and ownership of what is a heavy burden.

Fourth, you may think that your own uniqueness is tied up in your identity. Really your identity hides or masks what is special and unique about you.

Fifth, there is very little agreement out there that who you are is essentially spirit or soul. People would look at you as if you were crazy, if you went around stating, "Hi, I'm the space of pure potential".

Sixth, it requires a certain degree of humility or humbleness to believe that you are just like your brethren, not superior as your identity might have assumed. It may hurt to realize that there is nothing personal about your essence. In your essential state, you are pure potentiality.

I can hear Ron (not his real name), a member of my group, in the back of my mind saying, "Sure Doc, now when I meet someone new, I'll just introduce myself as the space of possibilities, the mother of all contexts, the creator of the screen that life shows up on. If I'm lucky, she won't have me committed to a mental ward. Why can't I just be more conventional in my response to her? Besides, I think that she would like my personality and be interested in my story."

What I am suggesting, in no way limits Ron from presenting himself the way he sees himself. The problem is that Ron may not realize that he is so much more than the contents and story of his life. He need not present himself as someone who is very successful so as to convince himself or others that he is not inadequate as he may secretly fear. If he was no longer attached to his limited identity or ego, he would not need to justify himself, make himself right and others wrong, dominate to avoid domination or defend himself. He would realize that he was part of a grander scheme, connected to others, and a part of the universal flow of energy and information. He would see that underlying the infinite diversity of life, is the unity of one all-pervasive spirit.

There is no real separation between Ron and others. Feeling secure in this knowledge, Ron could give up his need for power, control and approval. People would be drawn to him simply because of his own unique being. Ron's security lies in trusting that the universal spirit is naturally supportive.

YOUR ESSENCE IS SPECIAL AND UNIQUE

You have talents and abilities that are unique in the world, and your purpose in life is to find and express those talents. Too often, this requires peeling away layers of skill that have been reinforced by financial rewards or approval from others, but which are not your true talents. For example, you may be a successful lawyer but not really feel that your heart is in the job. On the other hand, you may have always enjoyed music, but felt that you could never earn an income from it, or that you would displease your parents by pursuing your passion. You may have been so preoccupied with doing the "right" thing all your life that you may not have any understanding of what your true talents are. To discover your unique talent, try to remember what you do when you lose track of time.

Ask yourself the following question: What do I love to do? Make a list, but limit the list to those areas that create excitement in you at the thought of them. Then select the one that seems most important to you. Now make a list of the ways that you can express this talent and begin the process of choosing among these ways on a daily basis. For example, suppose you discover that your major talent is in music. You find that when you are playing, you don't have to think about what notes you select, but instead can be intuitive and unburdened by limitations. You might decide to write down as many ways as you can think of to express your talent. Perhaps you can form an ensemble of musicians, take additional lessons, or volunteer to play at church, or for your children. Try promising yourself (Keep the promise!) that you will play some fixed amount of time for each hour of work..

For me, the short list of things that create excitement have to do with making a difference in others. I decided that the best way for me to do this was to write a book about my experience with heart disease. This book has been for me a labor of love.

CHOOSING TO OPERATE FROM YOUR ESSENCE RATHER THAN YOUR IDENTITY

At any given moment you have the choice in who you are going to be. You may choose to behave consistent with your identity or personality, or you may choose to operate from your essence. When you choose to allow yourself to be run by your identity, you fall into a trap of justification, self-righteousness, domination and control, characteristics based on fear and your history. When you choose to operate from your essence, you choose to trust in your gut level intuition and rich potential. You recognize
that you are connected to others and to a greater power, that you are not alone and that there is nothing to fear. Examples of these choice points occur daily. Just ask yourself the question, "Is it best to be consistent with my past point of view, or do I want to create a new future?" If you are satisfied with how your health and your life turned out, then choose the past. If you would like to make the kind of profound changes I believe are necessary to heal the heart, then choose a new future.

WHAT WE HAVE LEARNED

There is a painful existential dilemma we all face—namely the inevitability of our own death. To avoid confronting this unpleasant reality, we distract ourselves in a number of ways. We busy ourselves with "doing" and "having". We get in ruts, anaesthetizing ourselves by habit. We focus upon acquiring wealth, power and control to divert attention from our impermanence. We form an identity, or ego, which gives us a sense of being solid, and develop a narrative or story to embellish and strengthen our ego. We become hard-hearted.

However, this story, which seems so real, is based upon interpretations and cultural conditioning. Yet the story, however inaccurate, has profound effects on your behavior. Many of the roles you adopt in life can be traced to the beliefs that show up in your narrative. Your attachment to your identity and story can actually retard your ability to experience life, relate to others, and be in touch with your spirituality. Your essence, or innermost "I", is pure awareness and potential. You cannot observe your essence, only experience it. Your essence is beyond any individual identification or belief, since it is the space or context in which your identity and your beliefs occur. It contains the screen of life, but never appears on it.

We resist recognizing our essential state of being for a number of reasons. We are attached to our identities as if our lives depended on them. It is frightening to consider the degree of power and responsibility we actually have. We do not have the perceptual tools to get beyond our limited senses. Thus we cannot see ourselves at the sub-atomic level, connected to others and to the universal flow of energy and information. We have unique talents, and can choose at every moment to behave in ways that are consistent with our identity, or to express ourselves by operating from our essence. By allowing your hard-hearted identity or ego to take precedence, you are operating from the past. By choosing to follow your intuition or gut level feelings, you are more likely to create something new. The possibilities for health and well-being are much more likely to occur by creating a new future, one which is not based on the "stories" of the past.

CHAPTER 11

RELEASING YOUR POWER

*Walk in the light of your own fire, and in the
flame which ye have kindled.
Isaiah 50:11*

*It is never too late to be what we might have been.
George Eliot*

In previous chapters, you learned that you are not who you pretend to be. Your social identity, composed of roles, defenses and expectations that have been handed down to you by the culture you were raised in, is a mask that prevents others, as well as yourself, from seeing deeply into your essential nature or soul. Thus you cannot be accurately categorized by your personality or classified by your defensive attempts to prove to yourself or others that you are worthwhile. Nor are you a separate and isolated entity, needing to defend yourself from others who might harm you, since you are deeply connected to others at the quantum level and to a higher power as well.

You are the raw potential to be anything that you truly want. Once you begin to glimpse that life is a creative process, with you in control of how it turns out, you open yourself up to the power within you. You become captain of your own ship and master of your fate. But to do this requires that you accept responsibility for what you have in the present, even if no one in his right mind would accept that heart disease is something that a) could be chosen in the first place, and b) that you would choose to have it. Most people would see themselves as victims of an unwanted illness; an alien disease that was somehow thrust upon them like an uninvited guest or intruder. "It was my genes that did it to me.", or it was "just my fate". If you can get yourself to the point that you can see how you contributed to your own condition, then you can begin to tap the power within you to heal. Did you choose to eat the wrong foods, smoke, carry out a life which put distance between yourself and others, not take time to smell the roses, make others wrong, dominate to avoid domination, maintain rigid beliefs, feel sorry for yourself, or dwell on the negative? Were you a tough customer with a hard-heart who was difficult to get close to? Any of these and other behaviors can be thought of as being under your own control or responsibility. You may not have chosen well, you may have been lazy or defensive, or not psychologically-minded, or unconscious much of the time, but you are still responsible for how your life turns out. You have had something to do with your disease and therefore have a large say in its progression or regression.

WHAT IS PERSONAL POWER?

Personal power is the natural state of being, devoid of preconceived notions about reality and defensive postures. It is a "just is" position, free of blame, shame, or guilt. Power is not something that comes from the outside or can be taught. Rather power is realized. You are most powerful when you operate from your essential nature, doing what turns you on and lights you up. Joseph Campbell referred to this as "Following your bliss." He would teach his students to "go where your body and soul want to go. When you have the feeling, then stay with it, and don't let anyone throw you off. Learn to recognize your own depth." Operating this way makes you the creator of your own life, like the artist with a paintbrush and a blank canvas.

We have came to think of the world as driven by causes and effects. For every cause, for every impetus, there is a corresponding effect or reaction. Human beings, too, can be seen as living in a world of personal causes and effects. If you were a painter, you would be at "cause" with respect to how a painting turns out because you are the artist. In writing this book, I have responsibility for its quality and even for whether it is well-received or not.

But we need to understand, here, that *Cause* is not the same as *Blame*. If you are driving along, obeying the speed limit and a child darts out in front of you, and you strike the child, you would be the cause, but you would not be at <u>fault</u> in hitting the child. Thus, we can see, that we are responsible for how our lives turn out, but not to blame when things turn out differently from what we had hoped or planned for.

Whether you find your present life teeming with baubles, or beset by debt, whether you are in the prime of good health, or reeling from illness, operating from "cause" puts you in the accountable position. To be otherwise, would make you a victim of your own life, at the "effect" of forces seemingly outside your control.

It is not easy to see yourself as "cause" in your own life. We are accustomed to seeing circumstances as more powerful than we, and as dictating how we respond. For example, if your boss told you that he had to let you go because business was off, you might feel at the effect of the circumstance called "downturn in the economy". You would feel victimized, powerless and probably hurt or angry. To regain your power, you would have to take some responsibility for what happened, however unpalatable or embarrassing that may be. Perhaps you could admit to yourself that you did not contribute effectively to the company's bottom line, and that if you had it to do over again, you might work a little harder or smarter.

To help you see yourself as "cause" in your disease there are some difficult questions you can ask. You might ask, "How did my unconscious failure to take my medications contribute to my disease?" Or ask yourself, "How did my addiction to achievement impact my health?" You might easily answer, "You mean the seventy-hour weeks? No vacation in ten years? Not watching my kids grow up?" Or ask yourself, "How did my lack of communication with my spouse add to my anxiety and anger?" On the surface, this would seem to be a simple exercise, but as we all know, our addictions to things which are bad for us are very strong. Very few of us seem able to understand ourselves well enough to avoid our individual pitfalls to our health and happiness. But all of us can learn.

WHY IS PERSONAL POWER SCARCE?

People are taught that parents, teachers, doctors, and other authorities know what is best for us. We learn to give up our personal power to please authority figures and feel protected by them. Our training begins very early in life. As children, we are told not to touch the stove, not to play with matches, never to run with a stick in your hand, and countless other admonitions designed to keep us whole. In school we are taught to stand in line, raise our hands if we want something, and many other rules designed to keep order. Transgressions usually are met with negative consequences, such as a burnt hand or a detention.

Submission to authority continues to be reinforced by society through adulthood. We learn that it may not be wise to tell the boss what we really think, and it may be better to pay our rent on time. While many of the rules we have learned and the morès we have followed have survival value, if we have allowed ourselves to sink to a level of blind obedience, we are no longer living our own lives. Submissiveness to authority is useful in certain cases, in the army for example, or in a dangerous situation which requires a leader, but it can become an obstacle to taking personal responsibility when it is appropriate. Worse, as we have seen in a previous chapter, it can lead to resistance, non-compliance and self-destructive failure to follow important, even life-prolonging recommendations. Excessive dependency on external sources can also lead to low self-esteem and blame when things go wrong. Missed opportunities for healing are often the result of excessive dependence on seemingly-powerful others, at the expense of releasing your own healing power.

THE POWER OF LOVE

It has been said that "love makes the world go around." Songs have proclaimed love as the source of most of what is good about the world. And we know in our hearts, just how powerful love is as a source of motivation. Who hasn't acted in a silly way because of love? And who hasn't experienced themselves as somehow more noble or spiritual or as operating from a higher level out of love?

Think about a time when you were in love—Do you remember how happy you felt? How the rest of the world went away when

you were with your lover? Remember your sense of well-being? How everything was possible? Life was good and nothing hurt.

The feeling of love came over me only three times that I can remember. When I was sixteen, my heart was broken by a young woman. I remember how much I adored her. I was so smitten, that I could hardly speak in her presence. She regarded my silence as strange and uncomfortable, and dumped me after suggesting that I get professional help. I felt as if my heart broke in half, experiencing such intense pain that I actually told my mother about what happened, a rare instance of personal disclosure. I suppose that it was this experience that dictated the course of my relationships. I must have vowed never again to put myself in a situation where I could experience such heart-wrenching pain.

My relationships with women were predictable. As soon as I felt close, I would pull back dramatically, confusing the woman until the relationship would finally fall apart. My first marriage was to a wonderful woman whom I valued highly. Only later did I realize that my marriage was based on an intellectual process; I had certain ideas in my mind as to what my future wife would be like, in terms of her appearance, education, background and religion, and my first wife fit most of the pictures. I finally realized that love was something altogether different. Love had nothing to do with my pictures or expectations.

The second time I experienced love had a more positive outcome, since it was at the birth of my daughter. I was flooded with emotions which I could not recognize—overwhelming joy to the point of tears, a literal swelling of my heart with pride, immediate fantasies of how wonderful a girl she was going to be—an actress perhaps, or a ballerina—love which was unconditional and all-encompassing. I often think, "What kind of person would I be today if I had always been able to experience that kind of love everyday, in all of my relationships?" I am convinced that my inability to do that is an important factor in what led to my heart disease.

The first time I experienced mature, romantic love was when I first met my second wife. It was a case of "love at first sight". Just the way she smiled, the sound of her voice, even the way she smelled could warm my heart. She hung in there for five long years before we married, while I went through my defensive routine of getting close, then backing away. It was her love for me that finally allowed me to "throw caution to the winds", and commit to her. I have been blessed ever since.

I have made great progress in sharing my emotions. I have softened my heart and removed many of the barriers that I thought were protecting me, but were actually harming me further. I can now purr like a pussycat. And when I roar like a tiger, I can trust my wife with my angry feelings, no longer dreading that I will be rejected or punished for saying how I really feel. I used to think that exposing my negative emotions would result in her getting back at me somehow. Now I see that feelings disappear as soon as they are shared, and that I am "forgiven" for having the feelings. I also realize that I am in a better position to problem solve once my feelings are on the table. I can now tell my wife that I love her without feeling uncomfortable. Before, I would hold back, thinking that the words were too special to waste on momentary feelings, or that my feet would be held to the fire if later behaviors were unloving. Now I recognize that no harm is done, and in fact, positive things occur when I "risk" sharing my loving feelings. In fact it seems that the more loving I become, the more I get in return. This makes me even more appreciative and more loving.

THE POWER OF RELATIONSHIPS

Being able to share intimate concerns with someone also has beneficial effects on health. People who can confide in others are less likely to die than those who are isolated and alone. Among heart patients, those who participate in social and community groups are more likely to survive than those who don't take part. It has been well documented that individuals who are in loving relationships, recover from illness sooner than people who are alone. In a study published in the Annals of Internal Medicine, researchers found that individuals who had two or more sources of emotional support lived measurably longer following a heart attack than those with no support. Dr. Bruno Cortis states, "A sense of social support is crucial to the recovery of heart patients. Heart disease is a disease of loneliness and the inability to share oneself."

Many secretly-sensitive heart patients find it difficult to give and receive love. They see tenderness and sweetness as signs of weakness. Many are afraid of their own needs for love and affection. They pretend that they are self-sufficient and not dependent on others to any degree. Yet as we have learned, underneath that hard exterior is a warm and loving individual longing to get out.

To this day there are occasions where I pretend to myself that "I don't need anyone for nothing". Whenever my wife goes on a business trip, I am immediately reminded of the times when as a child I had to endure loneliness and a feeling of rejection. My reaction to this memory, is to automatically go into my "I don't need..." defense. Fortunately, my wife has learned to go beyond my distancing behaviors when she returns from a trip, seeks me out wherever I have withdrawn to in the house, and despite my lame protestations, gives me a hug or kiss.

I am still learning how to trust my wife with my feelings of vulnerability when she is away. Once I can tell her how much I missed her, perhaps we won't have to go through this ritual. I have learned that sharing my vulnerability with my wife has not resulted in rejection by her. I used to think that if she knew just how frightened I was, or anxious I was in various situations, that she would lose respect for me. This was when I thought she valued me only for my accomplishments. After many years of marriage, I finally "got" that she loves me for who I am, a man with vulnerabilities, strengths, fears, courage, selfishness, creativity, and a host of other positive and negative characteristics. I also learned that the more I opened my heart to my wife, the richer my life became.

THE POWER OF COMMUNICATION

Most of us have difficulty communicating, without knowing it. How often have you heard your loved one complain that you really don't listen? Listening seems to be such a natural and effortless thing that we tend to take it for granted. But listening is different from hearing. If our ears operate normally, we can hear our spouse's communication, but we may not process what is said correctly. We may interpret what she is saying and miss the point of her communication.

For example, my wife may ask me if I would like to join her in running some errands. That simple question would be run through a gauntlet of possible interpretations, before I would respond. Does she really want me to go, or would she prefer to go herself? Is she secretly saying that I should have run these errands earlier? Or does she merely want company? Depending upon the interpretation of the moment, I may or may not go along with her.

There are, of course, many times when I simply don't hear what she is saying, because I presume to know what she is going to say ahead of time. And there are times when I don't bother responding because I "know" that what she really means is different from what was said. I am smart enough to know that I make all this up, that it has nothing to do with the reality of her communication, but longstanding habits of suspiciousness and distrust are hard to get rid of.

We are always listening *for* something instead of *to* someone. Listening only appears to be a passive act. Actually we have unconscious filters which actively screen what information gets in. For example, if I listen with the filter "It's hopeless", everything I hear will be reconstituted so that it appears that directions or information is overwhelming or unachievable. Other common listening filters are "I know", "What do you really want from me", and, "No one can really like me."

When we speak to others, much of what we take to be good communication is actually something altogether different. Many of us are unaware, for example, that many of the "facts" that we share are actually opinions. "You will be back in the hospital again if you keep eating that ice cream", may be a heartfelt message from your spouse that has some basis in reality, but is an opinion rather than a fact. If it is stated erroneously as a fact, there is less likelihood that you will hear the message as one that is well meaning. More likely, you will feel put down or attacked. Much harm is done under the guise of constructive criticism.

Sometimes what passes as communication is actually empty chatter. Perhaps as a means to avoid intimacy or simply to pass the time, people may talk about things without putting their feelings into it. In such a conversation, the listener may feel as if she took a bath with her clothes on—she may get wet, but the warm, cozy feeling that a warm bath should bring is prevented by the wet, sticky clothing. In the same way, a conversation with someone who stays closed, who replays old "tapes", hides his true self, or avoids deep communication, may seem to be valuable, but in fact is unsatisfying and incomplete. It is possible that the conversation is so heavily laden with data that the listener may feel like falling asleep. This retreat into data may also be a way to avoid uncomfortable feelings.

Men, in particular, are fond of data-laden conversations. Many of my friends will speak easily of the stock market, their golf experiences, the problems with their houses, the newest features available in computers, or the best values in a sport utility vehicle. But getting them to talk about their regrets, embarrassments, hopes and ideals doesn't occur without the benefit of several glasses of wine.

THE LANGUAGE OF POSSIBILITY

Most of our conversations are filled with judgments, assessments, explanations, complaints, opinions, gossip, story, proof and politics, in the service of protecting and defending our position. Saying that "Mary should be more careful around strangers," is a judgment or opinion that tells the listener something about our beliefs or values. We may be strongly attached to this position, and turn red in the face if someone disputes it.

Stating, "Bill lost the race because he skipped practice three times", is an explanation or story which seeks to describe what happened in the past. We may become attached to our explanation and threatened if someone has a different point of view. Because "possibility" is distinct from the past, it is not about being right or wrong, winning or losing, or looking good. Rather, it is a creative act with no evidence to support it and with the outcome not predetermined.

When you speak about possibilities, there is nothing in the past to stand on. For example, if I say I am going to write a best-selling book about heart disease, I cannot draw upon my past, because I have never written before. The assertion may not make any sense when viewed from "reality". It is non-linear in that I cannot describe a trajectory which pictures my past and future writing performances. And there is no protection of my identity attached to my assertion. I am out on a limb, without a safety net, when I speak into the void asserting my intention to write a book.

When you have a conversation about information, there is something to stand on. You can be wrong or right, can appear to be smart or stupid, as you argue the merits of your case. But when you speak about possibilities—learning, discovering, exploration, and inquiry are your subjects, and there is nothing that you have to defend.

If you can get in touch with the difference between conversations for information and conversations for possibility, you will find that you are most excited and alive when you talk about possibilities. You may light up when you speak about moving to your cherished mountain home, or what your grandchild will be like when he or she grows up. Similarly, it may be quite exciting to discuss with your wife the possibility of resuming your hikes or bike rides with her as you continue to recover. Contrast these conversations with those centered around how much money to spend on a piece of art, whether or not to paint the house, or the merits of joining one or another Internet provider.

Clearly, conversations about *possibility* are more exciting, and far more fulfilling. Get in the habit of imagining yourself to be the way that you have always wanted to be. Declare that as your intention. Speak often about the possibilities opening up to you as you become this new person. The universe will support your intentions in unimagined ways.

THE POWER OF DEFENSELESSNESS

When a wild animal engages in combat with another of the same species, the losing animal will signal that he has had enough by exposing his neck. We forget that others fight with us because of their own fear. Our defensiveness is perceived by others as an attack, which causes them to be fearful and attacking. Being vulnerable allows others to relax and to be open with us as well. Although it is difficult for heart patients to trust others with their feelings, the risk can reap huge rewards in terms of warming the heart.

I used to be so concerned with my professional image that I would become easily defensive when someone asked me something that I couldn't answer. I developed all kinds of maneuvers designed to hide my perceived lack of knowledge. "Why do you ask?", was one of my favorite psychologist tricks. This question would often take the pressure off me long enough to regain my wits. I might then rattle on and on about something I knew about, as if to drown the listener in enough data that he may not notice that I couldn't answer his original question.

I really wasn't fooling anyone. People have a way of sensing when they are being hoodwinked. It was no wonder that others had such a hard time getting close to me. I was too busy defending myself against real or imagined threats to my professional image, to open myself to others. Later I learned to practice psychology in a different and more honest way. When I didn't know the answer to a client's question, I would simply say so. I would promise to do research if the question was important to the client, and this usually was received well. Later still, I learned to give up regarding myself as my professional identity, and for that matter any particular identity at all. I found that I had no need to be defensive, since there was no preconceived set of expectations that I required myself to adhere to. I no longer had to defend myself, because there was nothing at stake. In other words, since I was not defining myself in a way that had to be defended, I was free to be myself.

Resentment is a form of defensiveness that is particularly poisonous to the soul. Harboring negative feelings towards others for real or imagined misdeeds is most harmful to the heart. It leaves us feeling disempowered, victimized, and at the *effect* of outside forces. Try to get in touch with your own role in creating whatever seemed to happen to you that led to resentment and the feeling of being victimized. Try to get in touch with the false sense of identity that you felt was attacked, and let go of that narrow definition of yourself. In fact, if you can, wish for good things to happen to the person whom you resent.

THE POWER OF YOUR WORD

Most of us see ourselves as small in relationship to our circumstances. We let momentary inconveniences or temporary obstacles override our commitments to our word, and then wonder why our lives don't work out. For example, you may have been invited to an important social gathering at 7 p.m. On your way there, you get caught up in a traffic jam, and arrive at the affair an hour late. You explain to the host that traffic was at a standstill and think nothing more of the incident. These kinds of seemingly trivial day-to-day happenings often make up our lives, and leave us disempowered.

In the example above, other people made it to the social gathering at the appointed time. How did they do that? They simply made it their <u>intention</u> to be there, rather than <u>attempting</u> to be there on time. When you are <u>intent</u> on something happening, when you bring all your resources and power to bear, an Act of Congress could not deter you from keeping your word. This is in marked contrast to trying, which smacks of ambivalence, and is dependent upon circumstances. If you had regarded attendance at the affair as if your life depended upon it, you would have left early enough to account for all contingencies, including traffic problems, a flat tire, or any other seemingly large obstacle.

Many heart patients "try" to follow doctor's advice, and seem puzzled or saddened at their failures. They have lost touch with the power of their word, and no longer make declarations as if their lives depended upon it. Why not publicly state your intention to stop smoking and stick to it with all the ferocity and intention of a cornered animal trying to escape? Even if you regressed, your failure would be viewed differently by yourself. Rather than feeling guilty and disempowered , you could remind yourself of your higher goal and dedicate yourself again to keeping your word.

Health is a function of our integrity. Commitment means honoring one's <u>self</u> as one's <u>word</u>, and operating consistently with one's word. In my practice I saw a number of women with heart disease who seemed to pay little attention to their own needs, so concerned were they that others were taken care of. When I asked these individuals to let their needs be known at home, and to be a little bit more "selfish", they would leave the office saying that they would "try". Needless to say, they would be back the next week, with more stories of self-sacrifice and unmet needs.

Most of us feel small and unimportant. We have no idea how powerful we are. It may seem ludicrous to us that our pronouncements could mean very much in a world of billions of people. Who would hear us? Who would regard our words as important or worthwhile? Yet amazing things seem to happen when we state our intentions with clarity and force. The world seems to open up new doors once we have committed to a course of action.

My favorite quote is from Goethe:

> Until one is committed,
> there is hesitancy, the chance to draw back,
> always ineffectiveness.
> Concerning acts of initiative (and creation)
> there is one elementary truth
> the ignorance of which kills countless ideas
> and splendid plans:
> That the moment one definitely commits oneself,
> then Providence moves too.
> All sorts of things occur to help one
> that would never otherwise have occurred.

A whole stream of events issues from the decision,
raising in one's favor all manner
of unforeseen incidents and meetings
and material assistance
which no person could have dreamt
would come their way.
Whatever you can do, or dream you can, begin it.
Boldness has genius, power, and magic in it.
Begin it now.

When you make a declaration, for example to take charge of your health, you are committing yourself to your vision of the future. It takes nothing but your word to have your vision become a reality. You do not need consensus, or agreement, or logic to live into a future that you design, only your commitment or word. In other words, there may be no logical reason for anyone to believe you when you state that you are having *A Change of Heart*. But giving your word to yourself—committing yourself to your chosen course of action—will open up "all manner of unforeseen incidents and meetings and material assistance".

What should you do when you give your word that you are going to do something, such as sticking to your diet, only to find that you have regressed? When faced with a setback, try to get in touch with some of the automatic thoughts that you have in response to the setback. For example, "I always fail.", or "I'm just no good.", or "I'll never achieve my goals.". Recognize that these kinds of thoughts are from old tapes, and need to be disputed in light of your new commitments, and your revised ideas about yourself. After all, you <u>could</u> define your transgression as a "setback", in the context of a higher goal.

Praise yourself for setting a higher standard, and rededicate yourself towards accomplishing it. If your failures persist over time, review the possible "benefits" of your illness. We discussed in a previous chapter how illness can create such benefits as obtaining sympathy, avoiding unpleasant work, and serving to confirm a negative self-image. Perhaps your inability to keep your word over time is related to trying to make too many changes too fast. If this is so, try to slow down, prioritize, break down your goals into smaller segments.

Perhaps your body is telling you that you have to do things differently in order to be successful in the long run. Ask for help from your family to encourage you in your pursuits, and to confront you when and if you waver off course. Ask for time with the family that is totally unrelated to illness and will continue beyond the time that you recover. Remember to get in touch with the fact that the gains that you have made so far are the results of your own efforts, and that you are to be acknowledged for that.

TRANSFORMATION

A person who has released the power within himself is a transformed individual. This is different from a person who has merely changed. Change involves fixing, or doing more or less of something, or doing things differently, as for example changing your eating habits. That is a predictable and linear modification, such that you can chart where you were on a curve, and where you will most likely will be if your changes stick.

Transformation is unpredictable and non-linear. It is not just the acquisition of more information or a better way of doing things, *but a shift in who you are being* .

When you see the world through a new set of lenses, you have transformed the way in which information comes into you and is processed. You don't see people in the same way, and obstacles tend to disappear. People report a sense of rising above, or surpassing, or going beyond their previous self-imposed limits, perceived restrictions or confines. They feel no longer entrenched in a set of limitations, either by mindset, thought patterns, affect (feelings), behavior patterns, developmental stage or interpersonal agreements. Beliefs such as, "I must always be productive", impatient behaviors, and mindsets such as "I wonder what he really wants from me," begin to disappear.

Transformed individuals step outside of, alter or redefine what they consider themselves to be . They become different people. Transformed individuals experience a different sense of time from ordinary people. They no longer see the order of things as past-present-future, but instead reverse the sequence. Most people believe that their past determines their future. Even Freud said, "The child is father to the man," meaning that a person's childhood experiences determine what kind of adult he or she will become. Living a life based on past belief, however, is like mortgaging your future to the past.

A transformed person is not pushed into the future by past experiences or beliefs. He *invents* his future and, through visualization and intuition, lives his life in the present in accordance with his vision. The past no longer has the power to dictate the future, and remains only a dim, probably inaccurate memory of what happened.

This book was a future dream that gave my present life meaning and direction. What future do you visualize that you want to live into? Can you allow yourself to be pulled forward by your dreams, rather than pushed by your past conditioning and beliefs?

I know that you can transform yourself. I have seen it happen to my father, and have experienced it myself. Listen to your heart and allow it to direct you.

If we see ourselves as victims of coronary heart disease, and attempt only to change our lifestyle, thoughts or beliefs, we run a high risk of relapsing to our previous negative behaviors. But if we act from the position that we contributed to our conditions in several ways, we can shift from being victims to being heroes, from losers in life's lottery, to champions of our own making. Seeing ourselves transformed in this manner gives us a new perspective in the management of our disease, setting the stage for permanent changes to occur.

Transformation is possible for every human being, but to the heart patient, like you and me, it is the key to recovery—the entry to a new life of possibilities, free from the negatives which have ruled our lives and contributed to our disease. I am confident that together we can achieve new lives of love, possibility and joy.

AFTERWORD

The day before my father died, he called me into his hospital room. He wanted to share some final thoughts and feelings with me. With tears in his eyes, my father told me that he loved me. He was crying as he apologized for not telling me this often enough in my life. He said that he was proud of me and that I was a good son. I watched as my father transformed himself before my eyes. At that moment he revealed a side of himself that I had only caught glimpses of before. His heartfelt feelings touched me deeply. I had never felt such a deep understanding of who my father was, and such love for him as at that moment.

We heart patients are tough customers, and this book has not been easy for me to write or for you to read. I am convinced however, that despite our thick skins, and our rigid beliefs, we have the desire to experience ourselves at our best, to realize our fullest potential, and to be all that is possible for us. We know intuitively the difference between a path that has "heart" and one that is well worn through blind habit. And we don't have to wait until our last days on earth to begin the journey. By getting through this book you have demonstrated courage in the face of uncertainty, a willingness to keep an open mind, and at the deepest level, the ability to risk your own life. You have opened yourself to a way of being, which gives you real control of how your life turns out. You have your hands on the steering wheel instead of the rear view mirror. It may help you to review the exercises in the book several times, or re-read chapters in order to reinforce your intentions. And it may help you to ask your loved ones to read the book as well, to better support you in your efforts. Surrounding yourself with heart- warming people will make it safe for you to experiment with being yourself.

You and I have embarked on a journey of truth, much as my father did. This book has helped me, and, I hope, you as well, to look deeply inside ourselves for the source of our suffering and the seeds of our recovery. We have tremendous power within us to create ourselves anew. When we discover this power, we realize that having heart disease is not a death sentence. Rather it is an opportunity to heal very deep emotional hurts to our hearts. By becoming true to ourselves, we can experience the joy and aliveness that has been too long suppressed by the hard-hearted sides of our personalities. Everything is possible when we soften our hearts. We become fearless in the face of uncertainty or criticism. Our word becomes like law in the universe. And our lives becomes full of curiosity, enchantment and magic.

BIBLIOGRAPHY

Allan, R. & Scheidt, S. (1996). *Heart and mind, the practice of cardiac psychology.* American Psychological Association.

Barefoot, J.C. & Schroll, M. (1996). Hostility, CHD Incidence and Total Mortality. *Psychosomatic.*

—(1996). Symptoms of depression, acute myocardial infarction and total mortality. *Circulation.*

Booth-Kewley, S. & Friedman, H.S. (1987). Psychological Predictors of Heart Disease: a Quantitative Review. *Psychological Bulletin.* Pp. 101, 342-362.

Carney, Robert. (date unknown). *Depression affects heart rhythm.* In a study conducted at Washington University, St. Louis.

Caspi, A. & Moffitt, T. (November, 1996). *Behavioral Observations at Age Three Predict Adult Psychiatric Disorders.* Archives of General Psychiatry.

Chopra, D. (1993). *The Seven Spiritual Laws of Success.* Amber Allen Publishing.

Contrada, R.J. (1994). Personality and Anger in Cardiovascular Disease: Toward a Psychological Model. In A.W. Siegman and T.W. Smith (eds.). *Anger, hostility and the heart:* Hillside, N.J.: Erlbaum.

Cortis, B. (1995). *Heart and soul. A psychological and spiritual guide to preventing heart disease.* New York: Simon and Schuster, Inc.

Deikman, A. (1996). I Equals Awareness. *Journal of Consciousness Studies.*

Eaton, W. (1996). The Link Between depression and Heart Attack. Johns Hopkins School of Public Health.

Everson, S. (August, 1997). Optimism Decreases Risk of Heart Disease. American Heart Association Journal, *Arteriosclerosis, Thrombosis and Vascular Biology.*

Ford, D. (May, 1995). *Anger and Heart Disease.* Presentation at the Society of General Internal Medicine. Reported in *The Medical Post.*

Frasure-Smith, N. (date unknown). *Depression as a Predictor of Heart Disease.* Montreal Institute of Health.

Friedman, M. & Ulmer, D. (1984). *Treating Type-A Behavior and Your Heart.* Alfred A. Knopf.

Gullette, E. (1997). Mental Stress and the Risk of Myocardial Ischemia. *The Journal of the American Medical Association.* May, 1997.

Harvard Medical School. (November, 1996). Normative Aging Study. Reported in *Circulation.*

Jones, D. (1996). Psychological Rehabilitation after Myocardial Infarction. In *Outcomes Research in Review.*

Kaufman, J. (1991). Depressive Disorder in Maltreated Children. In *Journal of American Academy of Child and Adolescent Psychiatry.* March, 1991.

Ketterer, M. *et. al.* (January, 1996). Denial of Depression as an Independent Correlate of Coronary Heart Disease. in *The Journal of Health Psychology.*

McCrae, M & Costa, P. (May, 1997). Personality Trait Structure as a Human Universal. *The American Psychologist:* Washington, DC.

Muhs, A. (1977). Studies of Sociological and Psychological Factors Influencing Coronary Heart Diseases. Zeitschrift fur Psychosomatische Nedizin und Psychoanalyse. Gottingen.

Ornish, D. (1990). *Dr. Dean Ornish's Program for Reversing Heart Disease.* New York: Random House.

Refat, M., *et. al.* (October, 1993). A Clinico-epidemiologic Study of Heart Disease in Schoolchildren of Menoufia, Egypt. King Fah Hofuf Hospital, Saudi Arabia.

Selye, H. (1976). *The stress of life.* (rev. ed.). New York: McGraw Hill.

Todd, R.D. (1996). Increased Prevalence of Alcoholism in Relatives of Depressed and Bipolar Children. in *Journal of American Academy of Child and Adolescent Psychiatry.* June, 1996.

Zeith, R. (1997). Norepinephrine Levels of Depressed Patients. *N.Y. Times.* January, 1997.

CONTACTING THE AUTHOR

Readers who wish to contact me by email can reach me at EMPOWER@voicenet.com. I hope that many heart patients and others who have experienced heart disease will join in providing stories and thoughts on the illness. Please let me know your experiences in reading and thinking about this book, as well.

ABOUT THE AUTHOR

Lawrence A. Decker, Ph.D. was born in Philadelphia, Pa. Dr. Decker is a licensed psychologist, a member of the American Psychological Association, and a fellow of the Pennsylvania Psychological Association and the Philadelphia Society of Clinical Psychologists. He spent twenty years as a practicing psychotherapist. His managed-care experience included serving as an Associate Clinical Director for U.S. Healthcare. Prior to that he was a Senior Executive with Medco Behavioral Care Corporation.

Dr. Decker lives in New Hope, Pennsylvania with his wife, Louise, and his son, Jay. His daughter, Elena, lives nearby.